1 | The Illustrated Encyclopedia of the Animal Kingdom

The Illustrated Encyclopedia of the *Animal Kingdom*

The Danbury Press

Editorial direction and supervision for the English language
edition by PERCY KNAUTH.

Associate Editor–DALE MCADOO.

Art direction and Design by JACK JAGET.

Editorial consultant for volume 1 — Georg Zappler.

The Danbury Press, a division of Grolier Enterprises, Inc.

Publisher–ROBERT B. CLARKE.
Marketing Director–ROBERT G. BARTNER.
Creative Director–GILBERT EVANS.
Publishing Consultant–DAVID MENDELSOHN.

Library of Congress Catalog Card Number 71-141898
© 1970, 1971   Fratelli Fabbri Editori, Milan
All rights reserved.
No portion of this book may be reproduced without written consent.
The Illustrated Encyclopedia of the Animal Kingdom has been
translated and adapted from *Gli animali e il loro mondo,*
originally published in Italy under the direction of Professor
Antonio Valle, Director of the Museum of Natural Science, Bergamo.

Printed in the United States of America

PHOTO CREDITS

Atlas-Vienna-Bavaria—130; Australian News & Information Bureau-Canberra—68, 93; Barnaby's Picture
Library-Nash—13, R. W. Kennedy—14, S. Kalman—60, 88; A. E. Brehn-Turin—102; Bruce Coleman LTD-J.
Van Wormer—25, 43, 130; R. Die—111; E. Dulevant-Turin—93, 144; E. P. S.—104, 105, 143; Lucio Gaggero
—32, 62, 67, 85, 98; G. S. Giacomelli-S. Chiara-Naples—115, 141; Como Guissani—117; Igmar Holmasen-
Malmkoping—40; Institute of Geology and Paleontology—83; Institute for Scientific Research, Luiro—82,
93; Royal Institute of Natural Sciences-Brussels—123; Jesse—44, 58; Frank Lane-H. H. Schroeder—83;
Christian Lederer-Bavaria—69; Liedmann-Bavaria—106, 122; Longo—69; Zigmund Leszczynski—104, 105;
R. Maltini—22, 140; Marconato—16, 17; A. Margicco—11, 16, 18, 19, 24, 30, 34, 35, 45, 51, 53, 57, 63, 65, 69,
72, 76, 89, 99, 103, 112, 115, 117, 132, 133, 137, 138, 139; G. Mazza—14, 15, 28, 29, 31, 65, 83, 110, 112, 115, 143;
Monaco Aquarium—80; Marineland Aquarium-Palos Verdes—110; Manfred Melde—101; Museum of
Natural History-Milan—112; Hauff Museum-Holzmaden-Wurttemberg—70; N. H. P. A.-Betsoms-Anthony
Bannister—14, 15; J. Blossom—14, 105; Lionel E. Day—73; Natural History Photo Agency-S. Dalton—
59, 129; Oischki, Florence—30; Carl E. Ostmam-Bromma—69; Pasotti—26; Dr. Lino Pellegrini—18, 19,
71, 110, 143; CCM General Biological Inc.—16, 17; Willis Petersox—46, 91, 131; Picturepoint—94, 95;
Paul Popper-London—69, 73, 79, 95, 97, 108, 127; A. Pozzi—16, 17, 25, 33, 35, 84, 93, 103, 117; Relini—
141; Photo Researchers-Hillingdon—11, Des Bartlett—26, 47, 109, 119, 131, 135, J. Burton—37, 67, 116,
118, 139; Rod Allin—50, J. Dermid—73, Peter Jackson—108, Russ Kinne—41, N. Myers—136, Simon—
72; Roebild, Muller—12, 13, 39, 41, 87, 125; Roloc, Washington—100, 134; A. P. Rossi—69, 76, 81, 84, 87,
126, 129; G. Rossi-Institute of Botanical Science, University of Milan—20, 21; Miami Seaquarium—48, 81,
139; S. E. F., Turin—18, 19, 81, 123, 126, 127; Sirman, Dimt—78, 86, 114, 134; Misa Susini—89; Anton
Thau-Bavaria—10, 38, 123, 124; American Museum of Natural History—35; British Museum of Natural
History—66; Turbilder Okapia—18, 19, 36, 37, 50, 55, 56, 61, 73, 78, 84, 89, 101, 104, 125, 137; Tomisch
—56; V-Dia-Verlag-Heideberg—43; G. Vecchia—48, 107; Peter Ward—90; D. P. Wilson—18, 19, 31, 70, 108,
141, 142; ZFA Dusseldorf—25, 42, 88, 90; Frankfurt Zoo—9, 72, 92, 103; Roma Zoo—20, 21; M. Wiedman—
2, 3, 5, 45, 47, 86, 121, 137.

Contents

Foreword

*M*ost people find the animal world fascinating, and the intricate and graceful shapes of shells, the bright colors and airy grace of butterflies, and the songs and beauty of birds have their dedicated admirers and hobbyists. Until now, such interest has been largely of entertainment value, and our zoos, aquariums, and natural history museums report ever-increasing numbers of visitors who are intrigued with the form, the function, and the behavior of the myriad animals that share this planet with man. But now that man's burgeoning population is threatening this animal life, and with it the very existence of man, these same creatures may be the source of solutions to our problems.

Many of our rivers and lakes, once clear and teeming with life, are now chemical cesspools intolerant of life. Our once fertile fields are now sterile, sustained only by artificial fertilizers, and are used for crops that survive only by the dubious protection of more chemicals—herbicides and insecticides. All these poisons find their way into our soil, into our water, and eventually into the seas, where they pollute the entire planet.

For every species that is endangered by chemical poisons, there is another that is threatened directly by man, often for the most transient of reasons. The great blue whale, the largest animal that ever lived on earth, now seems doomed to extinction as a provider of dog food, fertilizer, and a small amount of margarine. The lithe and graceful leopard, too, may pass from the face of the earth to provide coats to satisfy the vanity of affluent women. And the noble polar bear, the aristocrat of the North, is diminishing before the guns of hunters, to provide nothing more than a visible symbol of a man's self-questioning of his own virility.

With a world population that is doubling every thirty-five years, man is drawing faster and faster on the limited resources of the earth. He does not seem to realize that the destruction of the environment and the upset of ecological balances threaten not only the existence of other creatures, but also of man himself. A third of the world is already at the starvation level, and famine and pestilence once more present the specters of death for all mankind.

Ecological problems are not new, for they have existed since the beginning of life on earth. Every one of the animals displayed so beautifully on the pages of these volumes has faced and solved the same problems that now face man. Instead of being bent on the alteration and destruction of the environment, man must learn how to come into harmony with it. Man must utilize the same checks and balances that govern animal populations to come into equilibrium with the environment.

There is much to be learned from these animals, for most of the great technological discoveries of man are but crude duplicates of the refined systems of some other creatures. Bats and dolphins have echo-location systems far more sophisticated than man's sonar. Fireflies produce light virtually without heat. Whales can dive to great depths and return quickly to the surface without gaseous damage to their brains. Bees can see ultraviolet light, and rattlesnakes are sensitive detectors of infrared radiation. Kangaroo rats live their entire lives without drinking water, manufacturing what they need from the metabolic breakdown of their food. These are but a few of the mechanisms that animals have evolved and refined and which man has tried to imitate.

In these volumes, then, is more than entertainment. These are sourcebooks of natural experimentation that have stood the test of time, millions of years of evolution. Each of the structures that makes every species unique is an evolutionary refinement with a function, whether it be the hydraulic pressure system that starfish use for locomotion or the hairy baskets into which bees pack pollen. There is much, too, to be learned from the social organization of animals, whether it be the noisy, but unviolent clans of howler monkeys or the tyrannical monarchies of macaque troops. Each has its purpose and function within the limitations of the environment.

Here in these books is source material for the future of man. He is a relative newcomer on the evolutionary scene, and he has attempted to dominate and to destroy the environment. It is now clear that his concept of altering nature is leading only to disaster. The evolutionary message is clear: he must either change his methods or face extinction from his own folly. There are many examples in these books of how he might adapt to his environment, rather than attempt to adapt the environment to him. Instead of "man against nature" he must choose to be "man with nature," and to come into harmony and equilibrium with the natural world around him.

RICHARD G. VAN GELDER

Chairman and Curator, Department of Mammalogy
The American Museum of Natural History, New York, New York
September, 1970

*A*s humans, we pride ourselves on our great and intricate inventions, our works of art, our buildings and cities, and our ever expanding domination of the planet.

The animal kingdom can boast of at least as long a catalogue of inventions as breathtaking an array of form and color and certainly a much longer period of successful occupancy of the environment. As a matter of fact animals have been an integral part of the planet earth for several billion years and in the course of this time have undergone innumerable transformations. Today's animal species range from microscopic organisms to 130 ton whales, and can be numbered in the hundreds of thousands. If extinct species were to be counted, the totals become astronomical.

Animals live in the water, on land and in the air. They have mastered the most sophisticated techniques of survival under almost any physical situation that can be imagined. Their conquests extend from the polar ice caps to the equator, from mountain tops to ocean deeps. Animals have achieved environmental success not with tools and machinery, but through the adaptation of their own bodies and internal make-up. When swimming, fish use torpedo-shaped flexible bodies, powered with energy produced by burning food. Moles have shovel-shaped hands with which to dig. Birds solve aerodynamic problems by way of wing and feather. Heat regulation in mammals is accomplished through the possession of layers of fat and fur. On the more sensational side, bats use an ultrasonic echo-location system. Some fish produce electric fields with which to find their way. Bees perform dances when telling their hivemates about the distance and direction of a food-source. And birds navigate by using the sun and the stars as a compass.

The fantastic diversity of animal life could never be discussed properly unless arranged in some kind of a system. Zoologists have worked out large and small groupings among animals, based on similarities and differences in structure, development and behavior. To the layman, some of these categories make sense, others take a lot of explaining. For example, that flies and gnats should be grouped together seems fairly obvious, but that barnacles and lobsters are closely related may come as a surprise.

This encyclopedia covers in comprehensive detail, all the major groups of animals, their membership, their appearance and ancestry, their geographic distribution, their living habits and relationships to the world at large.

The first volume emphasizes the group to which man belongs, the animals with backbones. It is meant to provide a general overview, understanding and appreciation of our closest relatives *in the animal kingdom. What will emerge is that there are certain basic requirements for successful living. These always involve coping and fitting in with the environment. Food has to be obtained, enemies avoided, and the next generation provided for. The cycle is always the same—from birth to parenthood to death—and in the process new life is born. And although the problems are always the same, the solutions of body shape and living habit are quite different.*

Animals with Backbones

The two sprightly animals below, one a song bird, the other a squirrel, typify the generally alert, active nature of vertebrates. The Old World bulbul is, of course, a flier as well as a hopper on branches.

Asking their children to show some backbone is a favorite request on the part of parents who wish their offspring to respond in a positive way to some existing problem. It is really a very appropriate phrase, for humans are creatures with backbones, along with fish and frogs, lizards and polar bears. And the hallmark of animals with backbones is that they are active, muscularly well-coordinated types that cope well with the environmental situation. As a matter of fact, they have managed to be extremely successful forms of life for some 500 million years by virtue of their particular anatomical configuration.

Animals with backbones are called vertebrates, from the possession of a column of jointed bony segments, the vertebrae, running along the back. This structure lends a great deal of flexible support to the whole length of the body and allows for the attachment of the other bones of the skeleton and in turn the many kinds of muscles that it takes to flex and bend, to run and jump, to be a sinuous fish or a two-legged human.

No great zoological know-how is required to pick out the vertebrates from the rest of the animal kingdom buzzing, crawling, and scurrying around us. That fleshy kind of skin-covered body with its internal skeleton and its generally graceful movements is almost always immediately recognizable. The trout in the brook, the splashing frog, the bird on the wing, the purring cat, the dog straining on the leash —all these are obviously closer relations than the jellyfish, the butterfly, or the snail.

Long before there was anything alive on the barren rocks of continental masses, quite different in shape from those that we now know, the oceans of the world had already spawned a multitude of living things. Single one-celled animals, sponges, jellyfish, worms, and jointed-legged animals with soft bodies encased in crab-like armor had been flourishing for tens of millions of years before a small torpedo-shaped organism with an internal stiff-

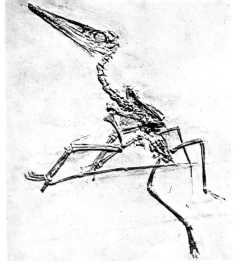

This 150-million-year-old skeleton of a pterodactyl (top) demonstrates an early vertebrate attempt to conquer the air. The long finger bone supported a wing membrane that stretched to the hind legs.

By hunching up, this tree frog (middle) is conserving moisture during the day. Later, at night, this amphibian will be quite active catching insects.

The yawning hippo (bottom) is not as lazy as it seems. It has spent the whole night walking and feeding on land and is now resting in vegetation-covered water.

ening rod running the length of its body was born to become the forefather of fishes, amphibians, reptiles, birds, and mammals.

The evolution of this stiffening rod, which later in vertebrate history became surrounded by articulating bony rings, can be compared to a great invention, such as that of the wheel. Once it was there, innumerable variations and refinements became possible. It took a fish for there to be an amphibian, and an amphibian before the reptile could be born. Birds and mammals both went through a reptilian stage before they became what they are. To go back to the wheel analogy—somebody had to invent a wagon before the racing car could be developed.

Look about and observe the success of the vertebrates. Despite the ecological mess mankind has wrought because of its vast numbers and generally sloppy technological ways, fish still inhabit the oceans by the millions and the croaking of frogs is as yet a common summer sound. Although the heyday of the reptiles passed with the last of the dinosaurs, turtles, lizards, snakes, and, crocodiles have managed to survive. Birds can be seen everywhere and exist by the thousands of species, although the pigeon and starling appear disproportionately

Among the surviving reptiles, snakes can be counted as the most successful group. Many snakes use poison with which to kill their prey. The deadly African green mamba lives below the Sahara.

On the open grasslands of the world, some birds have become adapted to a running rather than a flying existence. The ostrich (top) is native to southern Africa.

The mammals are the most recent group among the vertebrates to inherit the earth. Some, like the African elephant (at left below), have gone in for large size and bulk; others, such as this beaver, adding to its dam, change the environment as part of their living activities.

Crows (top) are aggressive birds, and this individual is scolding an intruder. The sharp beak reinforces the intimidating posture.

For protection this meek, clown-faced fish (bottom) changes into a bristling balloon. Stiff spines, now only barely visible, pop out all over its air-filled body.

Resembling a ferocious fairy-tale dragon, the iguana lizard (opposite) is actually a harmless vegetarian.

common these days. Among the mammals, we have destroyed many but favored a few—witness the dog and cat. We also raise plant-eaters such as cows and sheep to provide meat. The smaller rodents, mice and rats, have done well alongside man, and until recently forests and grasslands teemed with large to medium-sized mammals. Bison, zebras, antelopes, deer, and elephants browsed and grazed. They in turn provided food for the lions, tigers, and wolves. In general, then, the vertebrates, although they are but one of some twenty-five major groups or phyla which together constitute the animal kingdom, are a very dominant group indeed. They are part and parcel of any environment, be it water or land and, of course, they can claim *Homo sapiens* as one of their kind.

The trout (above) and the lion (right) are two fine examples of perfect adaptation to the environment. The streamlined, scaled body of the trout is obviously designed for cutting through the water with ease, while the lion has such complete muscular dominance over his domain that not even a tree provides an obstacle. The pig (top right) is not as handsome as his pagemates, but he, too, has mastery over his surroundings. His peculiar snout is ideal for rooting, providing him with food unavailable to many others, and his teeth, like man's, are able to handle a large variety of foods.

Shapes and Proportions

Other than sharing the commonly held characteristics that mark all vertebrates, the animals of this group are not much alike. There is a fantastic diversity of form. Although each has a head, a trunk, a tail, and two pairs of limbs or fins attached to the body, the variations played upon this basic theme are almost limitless.

Heads, for instance, all hold equipment for eating as well as for seeing, hearing, and thinking, but they come in a multitude of shapes and sizes. Some tiny animals have disproportionately large heads, while there are big, pin-headed animals that also do very well in their particular spot in nature. Some have squat snouts that barely protrude from the cheeks, while others boast long trunks. The head may be attached to the body by a long sinuous neck or by a scarcely perceptible joining to the back.

The body which houses the all-important digestive and reproductive systems is sometimes lean and sometimes fat. It may be capable of great flexibility or held rigidly.

Legs, which are the main means of transportation, can be massive columns, stilts, or paddle-like flippers. The feet at the end of those legs are sometimes clawed and sometimes hoofed. Some vertebrates are flat-footed with five toes bearing the impact of the earth, while others stand up on the tip of one large toe, with the heel raised high off the ground.

Lizards, mice, and dogs are quite different in external appearance, but all have certain similarities. Besides the backbone, common to all, there are also long tails, clawed toes, and an ability to use speed whenever necessary.

The word "fish" conjures up a picture of an aquatic animal like the one shown at the bottom; but the odd spiny creature above it is an equally valid fish.

Normally we do not associate flight with mammals, but the bats (right), despite their weird appearance and habits, are the one group of mammals to have completely mastered the air.

A tail, if you are a horse, is mostly a fly swatter; or, in the instance of the peacock, a great fan carried upward to attract the female's attention. The pig's corkscrew tail appears to function only as an entertainment for the rest of the world.

As for the external covering, it might be scaled, as in a fish, to allow for the utmost in maneuverability while protecting the soft flesh. Birds have an extra covering of feathers to provide insulation for the ever-warm body, while mammals have gone in for fur.

Extra attachments are frequently added to the top layer, like the horns of goats, the spines of porcupines, the antlers of deer, the combs of chickens, and the crests of lizards.

In each case, no matter how peculiarly the animal appears to be put together, there is a definite adaptive purpose to its general shape and all its particular parts.

All the animals shown on this page are atypical of their respective groups. Most salamanders have smooth, moist skins, but the rough-skinned newt (bottom left) has found its external covering useful in preventing dehydration during its long stays on dry land.

The indri (top right) belongs to a primitive group of primates called lemurs, but more closely resembles the much more advanced apes. Indris rarely descend to the ground, preferring the safety of tree branches. When they are on solid land, they walk on their hind legs with their short arms extended above their heads.

Sea horses are fish that swim vertically, rather than horizontally, through the water. They alone of all the fish have prehensile tails.

The small stump of tail carried by a rabbit is noticeable only when its owner is hopping away and displaying its white underside. Much more expressive are the long, sensitive ears, which may be carried up, down, or one in either direction.

Birds, among the most amorous of all animals, have developed various means of attracting mates. The lyre bird (above) and the pheasant (right) rely upon their beautiful tails to bring out the proper appreciation in their prospective mates.

The turtle, clumping slowly along in its shell, has survived for millions of years. The long-necked ostrich is flightless, but can run faster than most other birds can fly. The elephant's trunk is just as efficient a feeding and smelling mechanism as the dog's more conventional muzzle. No animal is ill-equipped for the life it leads. In fact, each has the necessary paraphernalia to render it perfect for its own special way of life.

We might, for instance, think of a lion as the ideally equipped mammal. The large head, held nobly on a well-proportioned neck, houses an alert brain and a powerful set of jaws equipped with frighteningly efficient teeth. Its body, rippling with muscles, and the long, powerful legs assure this animal of the ability to catch its prey. But the house mouse is even more successful than the lion. Mice not only live in more places than do lions, but they also maintain much larger populations than the king of beasts. They even manage to outwit man and to share his house and board. Mice owe their success to inconspicuous size, great numbers of offspring and a set of chiselling and grinding teeth that may not look as impressive as a lion's, but which serve the mouse very well indeed.

The extreme shape of the anteater's snout makes it possible for this animal to get at his favorite source of nourishment. The shoebill stork uses its grotesque beak in digging lungfish and turtles from the mire at the bottom of rivers.

The Realm of Water

The planet earth should really have been called the planet water, since more of its surface is taken up by this substance than by soil. Most animal groups started in the water, and so did the vertebrates, in the form of primitive fish some 500 million years ago. Vertebrates still dominate the aquatic habitats of the world, dwelling near the surface and on the bottom of rivers, estuaries, lakes, oceans and inland seas. There are more kinds of fish than there are kinds of birds or mammals, for instance.

Vertebrates owe their elongated, internally supported and muscularly flexible bodies to their beginning struggles in running water. And even though later many of them deserted lakes and pools to become land animals, the ancestral seas have recalled many a descendant of formerly land-adapted stocks. All of these secondarily aquatic forms have reconverted from legs to fins or flippers, and usually adopted a fish-shaped form. Well-known examples are seals and porpoises among the mammals, penguins among the birds, sea turtles and extinct ichthyosaurs among reptiles.

It is hard to imagine the oceans of the world without their grim population of sharks. The torpedo-shaped, broad-finned body of the shark (left), driven untiringly by the whipping tail, exemplifies the aquatic vertebrate.

It is natural to see a sea-lion (below) in the water as it is a fish. As a matter of fact, this descendant of four-legged land vertebrates has succeeded so well at the art of swimming that it can outswim the fish it eats.

Living On Land

Mammals are the rulers of the land in today's world. These zebras have legs and feet beautifully adapted to running on hard ground, and teeth that are well-developed grinders for the abundant grass they feed upon.

For about 100 million years, the vertebrates were strictly water creatures. Then the first amphibians changed fins into weight-bearing legs. Today's salamanders, frogs, and toads are their direct descendants. Reptiles added dry skin and the protectively shelled egg to the list of land inventions. A final physiological advance, the ability to maintain a steady internal body heat despite fluctuations in outside temperatures, always greater on land than in the water, was perfected by mammals and also by birds. Over the course of millions of years of evolution, only the insects have equalled the vertebrates in the successful exploitation of terrestrial habitats.

Amphibians and reptiles had periods of dominance in the past. Once gigantic "lizards" called dinosaurs ruled the land, but today's species, like the skink at upper left, are mostly small animals.

Amphibians were the first land animals, but even such well-adapted types as the toad pictured above still must return to water to reproduce.

This roadrunner can get around as rapidly on land as most four-legged creatures, although his class, the birds, usually concentrate on air travel.

25

Into the Air

The air can be thought of as the third major environmental layer, enveloping both water and land. Vertebrates first moved onto terra firma before flapping into the air. The most successful aerialists are, of course, the birds, descended from land-going reptiles some 150 million years ago, and now numbering about nine thousand species. Along with birds, another group of reptilian lineage, the pterosaurs, also managed to rise aloft. But they lost the competition to their better-equipped feathered

cousins. Being mostly day creatures, birds have left the nighttime flying to the bats, a specialized mammalian group. The aerial habitat is always a temporary abode—used for fast travel, the escape from enemies, and the hunting of insects—since ultimately the pull of gravity reclaims even the most enduring of fliers. Hence, nesting and other activities require a return to more solid surroundings.

As mammals are the rulers of the land, birds are the masters of the skies. Beginning with a reptile ancestor, birds added feathers, converted their front legs to wings and took off. During times of migration, huge flocks like those of the snow geese seen at left are a common sight. Some of these enormous flying communities travel thousands of miles, seeking the climate suitable to their needs.

Because of an anatomical structure similar to a ball-and-socket joint, the hummingbird (left) is able to hover "motionless" in the air as he feeds.

Bats are the only mammals to achieve true flight. Using extended skin membranes rather than feathered wings, they flap through the night hunting for food.

Patents for Living

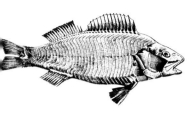

Among the vertebrates, a trout is obviously different from an eagle—one being a fish, the other a bird. Again, a trout can quite readily be distinguished from a guppy, yet both are clearly more similar to one another than either is to any bird. Zoologists have taken these basic differences and used them to divide the major category "vertebrates" into subgroups called classes. Thus fish constitute one class of vertebrates, and birds another. In addition, there are three more classes made up of the amphibians, the reptiles, and the mammals respectively.

Each class has its own "zone of adaptation" to which are related a basic set of anatomical patents. These characteristics are fundamental to each class and have evolved as solutions to particular environmental stresses.

Fishes and Water

A fish out of water is truly out of its element. Everything about a fish is keyed to its particular adaptive zone. The streamlined body, the muceus-coated scaly skin, the whipping tail, the ruddering and balancing fins, all facilitate movement through water.

Like all vertebrates, fish are bilaterally symmetrical, that is the two sides of the body are mirror images of one another. This body plan is fundamental to that of all backboned animals—essentially a pierced cylinder with a food canal running inside from front to back and open at both ends. Above the food canal runs the spinal column, a series of interlock-

The external appearance of a fish is enough to make us understand why this class of animals rules the seas. The sleek, streamlined body and head propelled by the powerful tail are obviously made to cut through the water with maximum efficiency. A look beneath the surface shows a musculature that is fully as well adapted as the covering scales.

The sturgeon (below), considered "primitive" in the total picture of fish evolution, is nevertheless in complete command of his environment.

ing discs called vertebrae that lend internal support to the body. Above the vertebral column, and enclosed by outgrowths from each disc, lies the central nerve cord. The brain is a ballooning out of the nerve cord at the front end. Protecting this vital cordinating center is a bony capsule, the cranium, to which is joined the first vertebra of the spinal column. The body cylinder is made up of similar segments of muscle fibers repeated from end to end. The propulsive forces that move a fish through water are produced by the serial contraction of these muscles, placed on either side of the solid vertebral column. The muscle fibers in each segment run from front to back, so that when they contract they bend the body. During swimming, the contraction of each segment takes place after that in front. In this

Swimming, for a fish, means curving the body from side to side as it moves through the water.

Trout like the one above are beautifully adapted fresh-water fish. For centuries they have been a favorite game and food fish of mankind.

Guppies like this lovely specimen are kept as favorite aquarium pets. This male with his long tail is much fancier than his mates.

29

Many species of fish lead communal lives and gather together in groups called "schools." Although they may be temporarily disrupted from time to time, they always fall back into position again.

Fish have adapted to every kind of watery environment. Some live in cold or temperate waters, while others, like the one below, frequent the tropical coral seas.

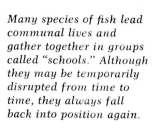

way, waves of curvature are passed down the body, alternately on each side. The large tail fin at the end exerts a powerful propellerlike thrust as undulating waves of contractions pass through it.

Most fishes have two sets of paired fins, the pectorals, just behind the head, and the pelvics, usually located farther back. Unpaired fins located along the midline on top and below are also present, usually, a dorsal fin above and an anal fin behind the vent. In general, the fins are stabilizers and balancers, with the pectoral also used for turning.

The front end of the food tube is the mouth, usually supported by hinged jaws that swing apart to take in food. Feeding can range from scraping algae to eating other fish.

To a fish, breathing means extracting oxygen from water at the same time that accumulated carbon dioxide is discharged from the bloodstream. This gas exchange takes place in the porous skin richly supplied with blood, that lines the gills over which the water passes. Many primitive fishes also had lungs for tak-

ing in gulps of air. In modern fishes, lungs have become an air bladder that functions as an internal adjustable "balloon" for regulating buoyancy.

The blood circulation in fishes is a relatively simple cycle with a two-chambered heart acting as a pump. Aerated blood flows from the gills to the organs and tissues where the oxygen is extracted. Deoxygenated blood then flows back to the heart, which contracts and pumps it back into the gills for more oxygen.

Although fish have no physiological means of raising or cooling their own body temperatures—these being solely dependent on the temperature of the water in which they live—they can seek out "preferred" environments by physically moving into warmer or colder currents.

Depending on whether a fish lives in fresh water or salt water, it has different problems of excretion. In fresh water, the kidneys must constantly pump out excess water to prevent the normally salty blood from becoming too dilute. In the ocean, the problem is just the

All fish are recognizable as "fish," but within the class, there are some striking differences. The pike seen at the left is a highly advanced bony fish while the shark, shown below in two of its 200-odd species, has a primitive skeleton that is mostly cartilage.

opposite; water is gulped constantly and excess salts are excreted.

Fish senses, too, are strictly aquatic. Fishes are adapted to see and pick up sound vibrations in liquid rather than in air. The sense of smell functions by way of a double set of nostrils that sample the water as it flows in and

then out. Fishes also have a unique sense, that of the lateral line system, which consists of nerve cells lining skin canals distributed over the head and body. By means of the lateral line, fish can accurately gauge water flow and pressure, a vitally important ability in their environment.

The "In Between" Amphibians

Amphibians can be considered fence straddlers as far as a zone of adaptation is concerned. This group, composed of salamanders, frogs, and toads, appears to hover between water and land. On the one hand, they have limbs for walking on solid ground, lungs or specialized skin for breathing air, and a sensory system that is keyed to seeing and hearing on land; yet for breeding most of them return to the water, where the young develop, and even for just plain living they all require a great deal of moisture to be really comfortable. But, from another point of view, amphibians can be thought of as perfectly well adapted to their particular zone, which is the habitat provided by any moist and wet condition on the ground or in bushes and trees.

Although it is generally misleading to consider the developmental stages of an individual

Amphibians made the transition from water to land with great success, but still return at frequent intervals to their original home.

In the modern salamanders, we can see how some of the earliest amphibians must have looked, but frogs have adapted far more radically to life on land. Forfeiting the tail while gaining strong hind legs for jumping made the frog's progress across land much speedier.

The salamanders with their eggs attached to underwater vegetation (opposite) are following the general amphibian habit of returning to the water for breeding purposes.

The male tree frog (right) is inflating his throat pouch to croak. During the mating season these "calls" bring the sexes together. Males and females will go into a nearby body of water to breed.

to be a recapitulation of its ancestry through time, the metamorphosis, or change-over, from fin aquatic, gilled larval salamander or tadpole to a four-limbed, air-breathing adult is very reminiscent of the evolutionary path undergone by the first amphibians.

A group of fish called lobe-fins are believed to be the ancestors of the first vertebrates to go on land. Pectoral and pelvic fins became front and hind legs respectively, attached to the spinal column by way of bony girdles. The spine becomes a strongly articulated but still flexible girder for bearing the weight of the body.

It is thought that the origin of land vertebrates was ironically enough an attempt to stay within the old adaptive zone of fishes, that is, water. As pools dried out during the drought-stricken Devonian period (some 300 million years ago), lobe-finned fishes would drag themselves over land for longer and longer periods in order to get to still-filled bodies of water. Eventually some of them became so well adapted for land locomotion that they forged the beginnings of the amphibians, feeding on early insects and spiders that had already colonized the land.

Although the earliest amphibians still seem to have had fishlike scales, most later forms developed naked, moist skins, lubricated by means of inner glands. The moist skin is necessary for oxygen and carbon dioxide exchange through the skin, which is a very important additional breathing mechanism for amphibians, even though they have lungs.

The amphibian's circulatory system is more complex than the simple cycle of fishes. There are the beginnings of the double loop system so characteristic of the more advanced birds and mammals, where oxygenated blood from the lungs is kept separate from depleted blood returning from the internal organs. In amphibians, however, although the heart has two separate chambers for returning blood, there is only one for pumping the blood out again, so that some mixing does take place.

In their own way, amphibians are a very successful group, numbering some two thousand species. Salamanders and newts are the most straightforward kind of amphibian, while frogs and toads have a body shape greatly modified for jumping.

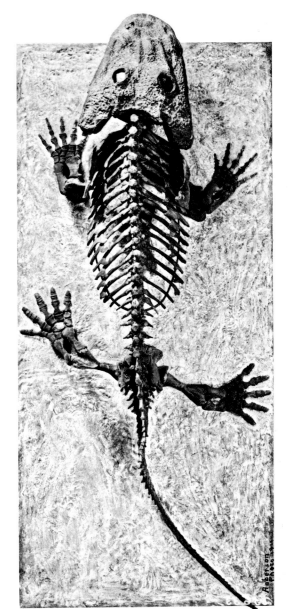

This skeleton is actually a fossil of an early amphibian from which scientists have been able to ascertain the evolutionary pattern leading from fish to modern salamanders, like the one shown below. Eryops lived some 350 million years ago and was about six feet long, with a heavy body and a flat skull. Eryops lived in and around streams and rivers, eating fish and lolling on the banks between feedings.

Xenopus, *the wholly aquatic frog shown below at left, has small curved claws on its three inner toes, which are probably used to dig out insects from the muddy river bottoms. Xenopus is famous as being the first frog on which human pregnancy tests were practiced.*

Reptiles and Land

A fully land-adapted vertebrate did not arrive on the evolutionary scene until the first reptile laid its shelled egg on soil. The development of land reproduction finally broke the amphibian tie to the water and opened the way to full exploitation of the terrestrial habitat.

The developing reptile embryo is still surrounded by liquid, except that this liquid is contained within membranes and a leathery and limy shell. This kind of an arrangement permits the reptile mother to lay her eggs on land. The fully-formed hatchling young have solid land legs that raise the body somewhat more off the ground than do the limbs of amphibians, although in most cases the legs are still positioned at an awkward angle sideways to the body.

Unlike the always moist amphibians, reptiles have dry skin, constructed of a leathery and scaly outer layer that has very few glands and that serves to hold in the body fluids. Along with fish and amphibians, reptiles are cold-blooded. This somewhat misleading term does not imply that these animals are particularly cold. What it does mean is that their body temperatures are dependent on the condition of the water or air that surrounds them, and that there exists no internal physiological mechanism for keeping body temperatures constant.

The turtle pictured here is a land species and carries the weight of its heavy shell on massive columnar legs, but it has relatives that are completely aquatic.

Monitors (below) are the largest of the modern lizards. Some reach a length of ten feet. Theirs is a very long history, with species very much like this one that flourished some 50 million years ago. Monitors live in every kind of land area from desert to forest and they are, in addition, excellent swimmers.

However, unlike fish and amphibians, reptiles perform best at relatively high body temperatures—muscular coordination and movement, the digestion of food and reproductive processes are all inhibited at low temperatures. To attain adequately high levels, the reptilian solution is not physiological, but behavioral. They seek out there warm rocks to lie on or direct sunshine in which to bask, thus raising their internal temperature; and they retreat in the shade or underground to cool off.

The chameleon (above) which looks rather prehistoric, is a modern animal, particularly well adapted not for life on the ground but in trees. It can change colors to blend with its surroundings.
The shingleback lizard of Australia (at left) manages to fend off enemies that can run faster than he by exhibiting a bright-blue tongue within a crimson mouth, a terrifying spectacle.

37

Reptiles first started to exist some 250 million years ago and soon became the dominant land forms. Some of them even returned to an aquatic existence. Their heyday lasted until the end of the Mesozoic era (about 90 million years ago), when, for still unknown reasons, their most impressive and seemingly most well-adapted representatives, the dinosaurs, became extinct.

Reptilian survivors, still quite successful, but now holding only a relatively minor portion of the earth's ecological niches, include turtles, lizards and snakes, and the crocodilians.

The breathing of reptiles is much more efficient for land purposes than the gulping of air or gaseous exchange through the skin practiced by amphibians. Reptiles use only lungs, with the air being pumped in and out by muscles located around the rib cage.

Reptile senses, too, are very well suited to out-of-water functioning. The whole middle-ear mechanism, including the eardrum, and already present in amphibians, is even better equipped for amplifying sound waves carried through the air so they can energize liquid-soaked nerve endings located deep within the skull. Land vision, too, is well provided for by protective eyelids and lubricating fluids that keep sensitive eyes moist and functional even in dry surroundings.

All the modifications in structure that fit the reptiles for a land existence would be useless without the development of appropriate behavior. This, in turn, depends on the structure of the nervous system. The reptilian brain is advanced over that of fish and amphibians in having the beginnings of higher centers in the forebrain that intergrate overall activity. In the lower vertebrates there are only separate centers, each center related to a special sense organ.

Although there are many differences between snakes and lizards, they belong to the same order. Snakes, the youngest group among reptiles, are actually descended from lizard ancestors. The loss of legs and elongation of the body makes the snake's movement across the land quite different from that of its relative, as is its way of life. Both groups, however, are highly successful land animals, with many species found throughout the warmer parts of the world.

The girdle-tailed lizard pictured here has a built-in defense against predators, such as its snake cousins, in the spiny tail. It simply coils up with its tail in its mouth, thereby protecting its soft belly.

The cobra (opposite page) depends upon the poison channeled through its fangs to kill prey and discourage enemies.

Into the Air

Birds have aptly been called feathered reptiles because in many ways they are still quite close to their scaly reptilian forebears. Yet, it is the possession of those very feathers that make birds the unique group that they are. The change-over from scales to feathers as a skin covering is tied to birds being warm-blooded vertebrates capable of flight—and everything about these fliers reflects their basic zone of adaptation, the aerial way of life.

Flying requires a kind of long-lasting energy and a lightness of body construction, neither of which typical reptiles possess. Warm-bloodedness or the maintenance of a constant internal heat level, independent of fluctuation in the environment, has been attained through a high rate of metabolism or bodily functioning. The highly efficient circulatory and respiratory systems of birds are a necessary adjunct since blood has to be well aerated and the tissues constantly supplied with new food and oxygen at the same time that the waste products are carried off.

Feathers function not only as insulation, retaining the body's heat, but also as efficient aerofoils during flight. In addition, downy feathers serve as a nest lining.

To lighten the skeleton, many of the bones are hollow. Instead of ponderous toothed jaws, a light but effective horny beak manages food.

The development of feathers led to the success of birds as the masters of the air. During the breeding season, male egrets like the one above grow additional plumage, exquisite white, lacy quills as much admired by human ladies who use them as adornments as by the female egrets for whose benefit they were devised.

With its brilliant coloring and swollen bill, the toucan (left) is one of the most easily identifiable birds. Despite its size and strength, this beak is extremely light in weight so it forms no encumberance in the act of getting off the ground.

All birds are recognizable as such by their feathers and their beaks. The structure of the beak varies with the feeding habits. The saddle-billed stork (above) acquires such food as frogs from shallow river basins by using its beak to extract the prey from the mud.

The fierce-looking eagle at the left is a native of tropical forests. There he uses his heavy, sharply hooked bill to tear apart the monkeys that form the major part of his diet.

41

The breastbone is no longer flat as in reptiles but carries a wide keel for the attachment of powerful flight muscles leading to the arms. The rib cage is reinforced with crossbars to hold it together during the strain of flight, and the bony girdle to which the legs are hinged is fused very firmly to the vertebral column.

The large brain emphasizes those centers that have to do with muscular coordination and balance as well as those portions that are related to instinctual activities, since so much of the marvelously intricate behavior of birds is fixed from birth, rather than learned by experience.

Prolonged care of the young after hatching is one aspect of this behavior that has been added by birds to the reptilian reproduction process.

There are over 8,000 species of birds in the world and if one were to count individuals, they would number in the millions. Some birds are solitary creatures, but some, like the murres on the opposite page, live and breed in large colonies.

Skimmers (above) can be found near seas, rivers and lakes in most of the warmer parts of the world. The long, pointed wings and flexible bill help to overcome the resistance of both air and water as they skim the waves in search of food.

The soft plumage of the owl assists in maintaining absolute silence as this hunter glides through the night skies in search of prey.

The Progressive Mammals

It is difficult to think of a fish out of water—a frog away from the pond's margin also seems incongruous, and although there are flightless birds, they are an oddity. Mammals, on the other hand, even if their progress over the reptile level of organization has been primarily in terms of refined adaptations for land, have become, by the very nature of their physiological advance, more independent of their immediate surroundings.

The mammalian organization includes many features that together enable life to be supported under conditions that appear "difficult." For example, a camel and the man it is carrying through the desert contain more water than the air and sandy wastes for miles around. This is possible because of the kind of waterproofing and elaborate storage systems of the warm mammalian body.

The faculty of maintaining a high and constant body temperature has opened to mammals (and birds) many possible habitats closed to the reptiles. Mammals attained their temperature-regulation system independently from that evolved by birds. Although both groups have developed the kind of blood and oxygen distribution system necessary to maintain their high metabolic rate, they have each assembled their systems in different anatomical fashion. The analogy would be two differ-

Mammals are the dominant land animals of today. However, many of them have also adapted to special environmental conditions. Porpoises, for instance, have become completely aquatic animals through evolutionary adaptation. Baboons, on the other hand, unlike their tree-dwelling monkey cousins, are completely terrestrial.

ently constructed engines both capable of delivering the same amount of power. Instead of the feathers of birds, mammals use hair for heat insulation. Both groups have separate circulatory cycles for aerated and deoxygenated blood, and both groups have highly efficient lungs. In mammals, the lungs function on a bellows system in which not only the rib cage but also the muscular sheet called the diaphragm takes part.

However, the really essential mammalian hallmark is the development of the forebrain or cerebral cortex. No other animal group depends so much on the responses to environmental stimuli delivered by way of this all-important coordinating and integrating center.

Cheetahs are members of the cat family, all beautifully adapted to life on land. With strong backbones, muscular legs, and powerful jaws and teeth, these are land predators to be reckoned with.

Mammals first evolved some 170 million years ago. The main changes from their reptile ancestors that can be observed in fossil skeletons consisted of changes of their jaws and teeth, as well as of the limbs. Teeth, instead of being similar throughout the mouth, became differentiated into the kinds of nipping, stabbing, cutting, and grinding teeth today's mammals possess. The lower jaw, instead of being composed of many bones, as in fishes, amphibians, and reptiles, changed into a single more solid, bony strut. All these jaw and tooth changes, of course, tie in with a more efficient chewing up of food—which again relates to a heightened way of living.

Changes in the limbs were all in the direction of pulling the legs up under the body, so that, instead of the crawling, sideways sprawl of the reptile, the true mammalian fore and aft stride during locomotion became possible. In consequence, the mammal stands high on its legs when it moves.

Another big mammalian advance is the mode of reproduction. Live birth of young nourished during most of their embryonic existence by food drawn from the mother's blood stream is the general rule (with exceptions); and after birth the young continue to be fed by milk. Also, there is usually an extensive period of care and training by the parents that is necessary for the more slowly developing and less immediately instinctual kinds of responses with which mammals adapt to their surroundings.

Mammals have spread out to take over every nook and cranny of nature in all parts of the world, from the tiny shrew at left to the huge African buffalo below. A large hole in the ground anywhere from southwestern Canada to central Mexico is a good indication of the presence of an American badger (opposite page) busily digging out rodents. Badgers are among the world's champion burrowers and can dig their way out of danger in seconds.

Elephant shrews (top) inhabit exotic locales like Tanganyika, Zanzibar, and the Congo. They are forest animals, hiding under logs and dead leaves, nibbling such food as insects and bird eggs.

The only mammals to have achieved flight are the bats. The little brown bat (left) comes of a family of 275 species, which has a worldwide distribution. They can be found sheltering in caves and tunnels, when not out hunting the insects they are so well-equipped to catch and eat.

The Business of Living

Feeding

Everything that lives must eat. Plants are able to derive sustenance from sunlight through special chemical processes that take place within them, but animals are dependent for food on other living things. The eating habits of animals are divided to provide a balance that guarantees abundance for all. Therefore, some animals specialize in eating leaves or grass or grain while some eat other animals. Each group has its own means of procuring, chewing, and digesting the food that is best suited to its needs. In no case does any one group of animals, with the possible exception of man, ever seriously deplete its source of food.

Great hunters can be found in every class of animals. The shark (above) and the lion (right) are both extremely adept predators. Although they survive on the flesh of other vertebrates, they eat only as much as they need and can be counted as constructive members of society as they serve to keep the balance of nature intact.

Hawks like the one shown here are beautifully equipped birds of prey. The strongly hooked bill is ideal for tearing flesh apart, and the strong feet, with their sharp, curved claws, also tear as well as grasp the prey. The eyesight is so keen it can be compared to a man with binoculars. The long wings help hawks to soar effortlessly for hours as their eyes sweep the ground to sight the mammals, reptiles, and amphibians that form their diet. With their great hunting prowess and strong preference for rabbits and rodents, hawks are mankind's most valuable allies in keeping down the population of those fast-breeding agricultural pests.

The Meat-Eaters. The business of meat-eating is somewhat more complicated than that of plant-eating. Vegetation is readily available in most parts of the world, and the animal feeding upon it has simply to wander about nibbling at random. Meat-eaters must put in somewhat more of an effort to find their food. This is particularly true of those animals that prefer a diet of other living vertebrates, in other words, the hunters.

Hunters must have highly acute senses for locating their prey and enough speed and agility to run it down. Most important of all, the hunter must always be more intelligent than the life it hunts. It is this superior intelligence that makes these animals particularly interesting to mankind.

Each group of animals has its own hunters. Most fish hunt and eat each other. Anyone keeping tropical fish in an aquarium can ap-

Hunting live food requires keen senses, persistence, and intelligence superior to that of the victim. The owl (above) hunts by night, depending more on the sense of hearing than on sight. Lightning speed, silence, and deadly accuracy ensure the kill for this nocturnal bird of prey.

The capacious stomach of the bear requires a great deal of food to fill it. In addition to live flesh, bears eat vegetation and carrion, and have teeth suitable to a varied diet rather than to straight meat-eating.

Scavengers like the vultures content themselves with carrion rather than fresh meat. Like garbage collectors, vultures are scorned by the general populace, and yet are absolutely essential to their environment. Some vultures have a wing spread of almost ten feet, while others are only chicken-sized. All but one species have naked heads. Unlike their relatives, the eagles and hawks, vultures have weak, blunt toes. Despite the great size of the griffon vultures shown here, they never kill, but eat only dead meat, which includes any human corpse available. When they are through with this zebra, the minute fragments of flesh left on the bones will be quickly consumed by other scavengers such as carrion-eating beetles.

preciate the predatory nature of these small vertebrates. But of all the watery hunters, sharks seem particularly well-equipped for the business of the hunt. The sleek figure of the shark and the silence with which it glides through the waters make its presence ever ominous.

Among reptiles, the crocodile is a notorious killer, and snakes do so much to keep down the rodent population that, in many tropical locations, they are kept as household pets.

As for the birds, eagles, hawks, and owls are amazing to watch at their work. From hundreds of feet above, they swoop down on their prey with marksmanship any bombardier would envy.

In the mammal group, the big cats (tigers, lions, pumas, and cheetahs) are champions. They have all the skill and patience necessary to the game. The little weasel, too, for his size, is an unparalleled killer, as are his cousins, the bigger wolverines. And wolves and wild dogs are well known for their terrifyingly efficient pack-hunting techniques.

Obviously a hunter that lives in the sea is built differently from a land-hunter or sky-diver, but certain features must still be held in common. Sharks and cats have powerful muscular bodies, built for maximum speed. Snakes and weasels are suited for the quick, darting movement that takes prey completely unprepared. The sharp, cutting teeth of cats is matched in birds of prey with an equally sharp bill. In every part of the environment, the hunters are there, beautifully equipped to do the job of holding nature's balance intact.

Eaters of Insects and Worms. There are many eaters of meat that content themselves with smaller game than other vertebrates. These animals have found that the supply of protein available in the form of invertebrates such as insects and earthworms is far more abundant and easier to come by. In this way of life, one must have a different sort of equipment from that found in the big-game hunters. While the

senses must be acute, sharp cutting teeth are not as necessary a requisite. Any method of catching, holding, and then gulping down will do.

Insect-eaters appear in every class of vertebrate. Many fish dart at insects and worms—a fact on which fishermen depend.

Most amphibians are oriented toward small flying and crawling things. The frog has a specially built tongue that is kept rolled up when at rest, but flips out with great speed and marksmanship when a fly is available.

Among reptiles, lizards are particularly good at catching and ridding the world of insects. Most turtles like worms and will not pass up a fly or beetle either if it is unwary enough to approach closely.

The smaller birds are certainly great eaters of insects. This fact was emphasized when recent sprayings of insecticides killed off thousands of the best-loved songbirds.

Among mammals, most bats have made the

Insects are a source of protein easier to obtain than living vertebrates. That many small animals have chosen this diet is not surprising. The giant anteater of South America (right) is another proposition. With that much bulk to nourish with insects, only the fact that he is perfectly adapted to his way of life explains his preference. The front paws are powerfully clawed for digging into nests, and the tongue, which extends from the long snout a good eight inches, is very sticky. Each time the anteater sticks his tongue into the hole he has dug, it comes out with hundreds of ants glued to it.

The frog, too, uses its tongue to catch the insects and worms it eats. Frogs (opposite page, top) are among our most valuable insect exterminators, ridding the world of a large number of pests.

Lizards are also great consumers of insects. This beetle will provide a hearty meal for its captor (opposite page).

collecting of flying insects a way of life. Shrews and moles are worm- and insect-eating mammals with such a fondness for their favorite food that they live below the ground to be closer to the source. A specialization for the exclusive eating of ants and termites is not uncommon. The usual prerequisite is a long snout containing few, if any, teeth, and a very long, sticky tongue that can be pushed into underground nests. Strong digging claws on the forefeet are generally also present. Ant-eating mammals include the Australian egg-laying spiny anteater, the marsupial anteater, and several South American anteaters, the largest of which measures some six feet in length, a surprising amount of bulk to be sustained by ants. But this animal is so well-endowed by nature for the gathering of this food that thousands of these insects may be taken in with just a few moment's effort. Armadillos are also quite fond of ants, although they will eat many other foods besides.

Mankind owes a great debt to the insect-eaters of the world. Insects are, by and large, the most successful living creatures in the world today. Despite all the inventions of men, some more harmful than helpful, the insects

persevere. If not for the insect-eaters, insects would literally overrun this planet.

Parasites and Scavengers are disliked by the rest of the world. It is not pleasant to contemplate blood-sucking or picking at carcasses as a way of life. However, repugnant as these animals are they are a part of the ecological whole and act as a corps of sanitary engineers.

Among fish, there are lampreys and hag fishes, which, by means of their sucker mouths attach themselves to other fish, living off their substance.

Among birds, there are vultures patrolling the skies in search of death.

As for the mammals, vampire bats suck the blood of other warm-blooded creatures, and hyenas are renowned garbage collectors.

Although the animals mentioned above are anatomically suited to this specific way of life, there are, besides, many hunting animals which do not disdain carrion when it is available. Whether you are a fish, a turtle, a hawk, or a dog, finding a large hunk of meat in your path, in the form of a corpse, is a piece of good luck not to be ignored. One eats when food is available.

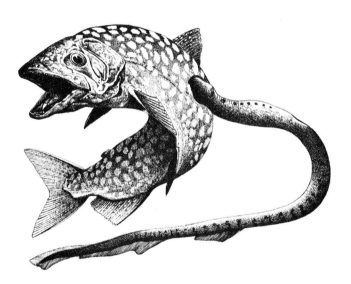

The Plant-Eaters. There are plants everywhere on earth. In the hot, sandy desert, one finds cactus growing and even in the frigid Arctic there is lichen on the rocks, and beneath the ice of the sea, there is floating greenery. The variety is staggering; from microscopic aquatic algae to the huge trees of the forest and the thousands of species in between. And almost all of them grow in abundance, for all that is necessary to sustain plant life is sunlight, of which there is rarely a shortage.

This abundance of vegetation has been utilized by many kinds of vertebrates. Every kind of plant is eaten by one kind of animal or another. As the diversity of plants is so great, the eaters of them are also highly diverse, with special adaptations that suit each for its chosen diet. The tiny hummingbird feeding on nectar and the large trunked elephant breaking off branches have little in common, but both are dependent on vegetation and have evolved anatomies suitable to their respective tastes.

Plant-eaters can be distinguished from meat-eaters by anatomy and behavior. While meat-eaters have sharp cutting teeth, plant-eaters rely on heavy grinding teeth or special bills. Because plant-eaters acquire their food in a passive rather than an aggressive manner, their bodies conform to their habits and they are built for defense rather than offense.

The pictures on these pages are a clear indication of the phrase "balance of nature". Each animal is fully adapted to a different sort of a diet, assuring abundant opportunities for all.

This practically limbless lizard, a kind of a skink (opposite page, top) has just caught a large moth and will make short work of swallawong it. Digestion will take a little longer.

The spiny anteater or echidna (opposite page, bottom) is an egg-laying mammal that lives on Australian ants.

The lamprey (center) is a most unpleasant primitive fish that attaches itself to other fishes with a suction-cup mouth. With sharp teeth, it then rasps its way inside, where it drains the body fluids of its victim.

The large deer (top) and the tiny mouse (bottom) are both plant-eaters, but the deer concentrates on grass and leaves while the mouse prefers grain and seeds.

Just as there are meat-eaters in every category of vertebrate, there are also plant-eaters of every class. Plant-eaters have to take in a larger volume of food to provide them with the necessary energy to exist, so usually more time is spent eating and digesting than is the case in meat-eaters.

While many fish eat meat, there are also many who live on vegetation. There is some plant matter in all water, even a still, polluted-looking mud hole is covered with green slime. That slime is actually hundreds of tiny plants clustered together that are commonly referred to as algae. And there are many fish that live on algae.

Young frog and toad tadpoles also eat aquatic vegetation, though as they grow larger their need for protein increases and they become more meat-dependent.

Turtles that live in the water also feed on

Hummingbirds sip nectar from flowers and are beautifully equipped for this activity. The wings are so structured that they are able to beat very rapidly (as many as 50 vibrations per second). Thus the hummingbird can hover virtually motionless over its food. Not having to bother with a perch, the hummingbird is able to flit from flower to flower taking a large amount of food in a very short time. Within the thin, sharp beak is a long tongue with a brushlike tip to which the nectar clings. Hummingbirds spend most of their lives above ground; consequently, their legs are too short to be of any real use in walking. In spite of their tiny size, weak legs, and highly specialized diets, hummingbirds are amazingly strong and adaptable. They inhabit forests, deserts, and snowy mountain tops from Canada to South America.

this vegetation. Those on land eat all sorts of plants, including those that grow in our gardens.

There are mammals of every description that are dependent on plants. Rodents eat grain and nuts, rabbits eat vegetables, rhinos browse on leaves, and cows eat grass.

In fact, there is a whole group of fairly large-sized mammals that live on grass and they are called "ruminants" for their special handling of this food. Grass is not easy to digest and goats, sheep, cattle, antelopes, and deer have compartmentalized stomachs to aid them in this process. But there are many animals without this advantage that manage to eat grass. Among these are horses and kangaroos. Those mammals that are considered browsers rather than grazers (of which rhinos, tapirs, and elephants are just a few) eat soft leaves rather than hard grass, and these do not have the cement-coated, highly efficient grinding teeth of grass-eaters.

Vampire bats are well known for their nasty habits, but very little is ever said about the gentle and charming fruit bats, who suck out the juice of such lush plants as figs, dates, guavas, and mangoes.

Like birds, bats are able to fly to their food. Fruit bats (above) have developed another birdlike characteristic—a fringed tongue like that of a hummingbird to extract the juice and pulp from their favorite food.

Rabbits live on a wide variety of vegetation. Considered a curse by most truck farmers, rabbits consume many of the same vegetables we enjoy and are well-equipped to do so with sharp incisors in the front of the mouth for tearing and strong molars behind for grinding.

59

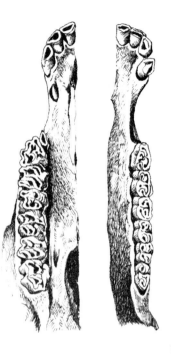

The Cuscus (above), a marsupial of Australia and nearby regions, is a tree-dweller and consequently eats what it finds there: fruits, leaves, insects, but also birds and birds' eggs. Horses (opposite page) are eaters of grass, a plant that is difficult to chew. But when the first grasslands began to appear, millions of years ago, some horses began to develop the sort of teeth necessary to chew grasses. The strong ridges and crests shown in the teeth above make ideal grinding tools.

Pigs eat many kinds of food, but what they are best suited for is the digging up of roots, which they chomp and turn into energy.

Even those mammals most closely related to man, the apes, are mostly vegetarians, generally disdaining animal food. More like man in dietary habits are the bears and raccoons, who vary their diets to include some meat and some vegetables, thereby enjoying all that nature has to offer.

Some of the specializations developed among the plant-eating animals are truly astonishing. This is particularly so among the vegetarian birds and mammals.

The bill of a parrot, for instance, is very powerful and hinged to the skull in such a way that tremendous leverage can be developed for crushing large and hard seeds.

Those other great seed-eaters, the mice, have front teeth that grow constantly as they wear down and are sharpened against each other to form an ever-sharp chisel, which operates most effectively against seed casings. Hummingbirds hide a structure very much like a ball and socket joint at the shoulder, which permits them to hover "motionless" in mid-air while sipping nectar from a flower. Also, these birds have very long tongues with brushlike tips.

61

Fruit bats derive their nectar from fruit in somewhat the same way. Using their long brushlike tongues to extract the pulp, they crush it against the palate and spit out the dry mash after swallowing the juice. Some species of bats have a special structure of the lips, windpipe, and gullet which forms a suction mechanism for drawing in fruit pulp.

The swallow-tanager has a broad hooked bill with sharp edges that work well in cutting up fruit, but it prefers to swallow it whole. There

There are thousands of species of plants and most of them are eaten by some kind of animal. Dormice like this one eat nuts, buds and leaves and live in bushes and trees to be closer to the source of their food.

The crow (opposite page, top) is just one of many animals that enjoy berries when in season. Foxes and bears are also berry lovers. In addition to this juicy food, crows also eat grain, making them a prime target for indignant farmers.

Deer (top) and yaks (opposite page) are members of a group of mammals referred to as "ruminants" because of a specially compartmentalized stomach that breaks down the grasses they eat into easily digestible matter.

is, therefore, a pouch, capable of stretching a long way, located just beneath the bill.

Pocket gophers also have pouches for holding food. In their case, these extend from the cheeks clear back to the shoulders. The basis of the gopher's diet consists of dirt-covered roots, on which they gnaw while sitting in their underground burrows. Their lips can close tightly behind their front teeth, so that dirt does not enter the mouth while gnawing. Manatees are strict vegetarians, feeding on aquatic plants and land plants that overhang the water. They use their flippers to bring the food to the mouth. The upper lip is split to be used as a forceps for picking up food, and heavy bristles help in pushing plants into the mouth.

Of course, during the berry season, when the smell of ripe vegetation is heavy in the air, even the most confirmed meat-eater may be tempted to join the plant-eaters for a meal or two. As a matter of fact, many ordinarily carnivorous animals gladly supplement their diet with plant food which is often more readily obtainable than meat.

Breeding

In the beginning, all life was in the sea and so the kind of reproduction that takes place in water is the oldest form in the world. Most fish still breed in the old way, laying the same kind of eggs that they have been laying for millions of years.

Amphibians, the first vertebrates to conquer land, must still return to the water to breed and it is here that we find their eggs and the emerging tadpoles.

To survive as an individual, an animal must solve the problems involved in obtaining enough food to maintain itself. The survival of the species depends upon reproduction. Of course, if an animal is unhealthy through lack of the proper foods, he is unlikely to breed or, if he does, will have inferior offspring. But providing all the requirements to healthy life are met, there are still specific obstacles to breeding that must be overcome. The greater the success in producing offspring, the more dominant the group becomes. Innumerable breeding problems are encountered in the various environments in which animals live, and each must be solved in a different way. The methods worked out to accommodate new life are many, but, in general, can be broken down into four large categories: egg-laying in water, egg-laying on land, live birth in water, and live birth on land.

Egg-Laying in Water. Backboned animals began their history in water; and egg-laying in water is the oldest form of reproduction practiced and perfected by vertebrates.

Fish that live in the cold parts of the globe have breeding seasons, those of the tropics breed at any time of the year. Some fish lay floating eggs, others have sticky-shelled eggs that become attached to plants. Others bury eggs beneath the soil or gravel at the bottom.

Most fish eggs, whatever the environment, have a yolk on which the developing new life feeds until hatching and, in some instances, a long while afterward.

The young fish are referred to as larvae,

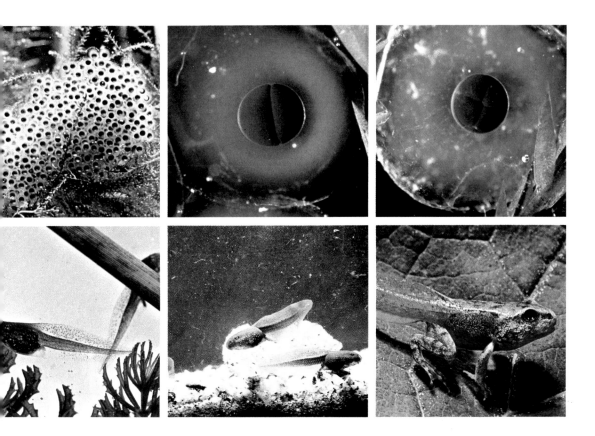

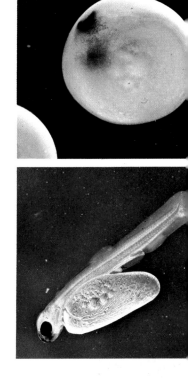

which means they have some transformation to undergo before they fully resemble their parents. In some cases they look so different that even an expert has difficulty identifying them.

There are intricate courtship rituals in some species of fish, while others are quite casual about the whole thing. In most cases, at the right moment, the female will drop her unfertilized eggs near the waiting male, who covers them with sperm.

Amphibians have adapted very well to life on humid land in all respects but one—the vast majority of them must return to the water to breed. Frogs and toads usually congregate at a body of water at mating season. The males croak their own funny song to attract the females. After pairing off, the male climbs on the back of the female, clasping her tightly around her middle with his arms. In this manner, they swim around until the female is ready to lay her eggs. When she is, she stretches out her hind legs and the eggs emerge at the same time that the male releases his sperm.

Most male salamanders have beautiful breeding colors and special scent glands with which to attract females. The male presents the female with a bundle of sperm wrapped in a jellylike capsule, which the female inserts into her vent. The female then lays eggs that have been fertilized by the sperm inside her body.

Amphibian eggs may be laid in clusters on the surface of the water or among the leaves of aquatic plants.

In general, aquatic eggs are laid in great numbers, of which only a very small percentage manage to develop into a new generation.

Above left, in the top row from left to right: (a) an egg mass in the water —each gelatinous capsule contains a single cell, which is the fertilized egg. (b) An egg cell that has split in two. (c) The same egg now at the four-cell stage. In the bottom row from left to right: (d) two tadpoles have hatched from their gelatinous membranes. (e) A tadpole that is beginning to develop hind legs. (f) An almost completely adult frog with only the tail remaining to be absorbed.

Above right: a trout egg and hatched trout larva still with yolk sac attached. The larva does not feed independently until the yolk sac has been absorbed.

65

Egg-Laying On Land. The first land egg was developed by the reptiles, making the group the first to be fully terrestrial. To accomplish this, an egg was devised that provided a small inner pool in which the budding reptile could mature, well-nourished by a large supply of yolk, while surrounded by a hard casing which protects it.

This egg, which took so many millions of years to develop, does not seem to be overly appreciated by the inventors, who, for the most part, do not bother with nests. Generally, the eggs are simply deposited on the ground with a little earth or sand scratched over the top. A clutch of eggs may number from under ten to more than sixty, depending on the species. Turtles use their hind feet to dig gourd-shaped holes into which the eggs are deposited. Crocodilians heap plant debris mixed with soil over their clutch. However, in all cases, it is the heat of the sun that incubates the reptile egg, even though certain lizards and snakes will coil themselves around their eggs for protection. When the young emerge, they are fully active individuals, looking much like their par-

The reptiles were the first animals to devise a fully terrestrial egg. Dinosaur eggs like those show on the opposite page have been fossilized. Discovered and studied by scientists, they show very much the same kind of structure that exists in a modern reptile egg like that of the turtle and lizard shown here.

ents. To aid in breaking the shell, each young reptile has a small "egg tooth" on its snout, which disappears shortly after hatching.

Fertilization in reptiles is always internal, male and female intertwining tails to bring the two vents into opposition.

Being primarily land-adapted, reptiles, even when secondarily aquatic, will return to the land to lay their eggs. However, for these water reptiles such as crocodiles and certain turtles, courtship and mating proceed in the new element. Crocodile breeding time can be a pretty violent affair with the aggressive males roaring and bellowing and on mating sometimes biting the female severely in the neck.

Mating in snakes is much more peaceful, with both male and female maneuvering their bodies to make internal fertilization possible. Some male snakes still have vestiges of hind legs that form a kind of spur, and with these the male scratches the female's sides as he slides over her back.

Birds profited by the reptiles' discovery of the land egg and went on to improve upon it with extra calcium in the shell. With the possibility of incubating the embryos inside the eggs with the warmth of their own always heated bodies, came a great elaboration of nesting techniques.

Nests can be woven out of twigs, grass, fur, or feathers, or they can be shallow depressions in the ground. Some birds dig tunnels; others

use mud or saliva with which to build homes.

Courtship and mating in birds are as varied as nesting habits. There are birds that are polygamous (several females to one male), birds that are polyandrous (several males to one female), birds that pair for one breeding season, and those that mate for life.

Most male birds have exquisite plumage they "show off" during courtship rituals that vary from species to species.

After mating, males may take an active part in nest-building and incubation or they may be completely indifferent. In polygamous birds, the males usually ignore the young, but care for the females. Polyandrous females leave the males to look after the eggs they have just laid and go off to find new mates.

Bird eggs may be round, oval, or pyramid-shaped. They are sometimes white, but more frequently are colored. The emerging infants may be naked and helpless on hatching or fully feathered and ready to leave the nest.

The midwife toad (far left) is exceptional in its child-care habits. Most amphibians lay their eggs and swim away, indifferent to their offspring's future. But the male midwife toad attaches his mate's eggs to his thighs and keeps them with him until they hatch. With most birds, on the other hand, it is the female (below) who does the brooding.

The picture opposite shows a new-born shark taking to the water.

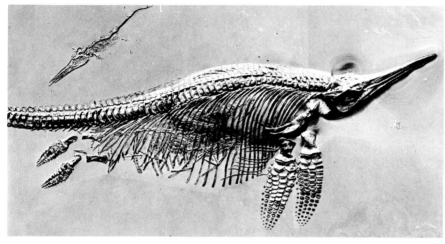

Live Birth in Water. Although most fish lay eggs, there are those that give birth to live offspring. Most notable of these are the sharks and rays, but other, smaller, species also do this. Guppies and mollies, the very popular aquarium fish, have tiny live offspring as do many of the perchlike fish.

Most live-bearing mother fish simply retain the eggs within the body, with the young being nourished by the yolk until ready to hatch. But some have eggs with no yolk and the developing embryos must be nourished by food from the mother's body.

The group that has perfected internal development, live birth, and later feeding of milk by the mother are the mammals. One does not usually think of these animals as courting and reproducing in water, but there are several that do.

Whales live their entire lives in the sea. They court, mate, and have their young in the water they call home. Among whales, the harem situation is usual, with each male allied with several females. Those whales frequenting cold waters swim down to warmer parts of the world when the young are ready to be born. The young are quite large, usually about half

Some ancient reptiles reverted to aquatic living and became completely fishlike in appearance. Because the terrestrial egg typical of the reptiles was unsuited to life at sea, the mother retained the eggs within her body until after the eggs hatched. The fossil ichthyosaur preserved in limestone was a female with live young ready to be born visible inside the body cavity.

Porpoises, like most mammals, give live birth. The young are able to manage well in the water from the time of their birth, with just a little assistance from the mother.

70

as big as the mother, and are born underwater. Mother whales usually push their newborn infants to the surface for their first breath of air. When ready to nurse, the mother lies on her side in the water, so the baby is close to the suface and can breathe. A fold of skin around the nipple forms a sort of valve for blocking out the surrounding water, while the baby nurses. Whale's milk is about four times as rich as cow's milk, so the young grow and mature very rapidly.

Sea otters also have live young in the water. A single pup is born at a very advanced stage of development, with eyes open and a full set of milk teeth, enabling it to take soft food almost from birth. Nevertheless, it nurses for almost a year. The mother floats on her back while nursing the pup nestled on her chest.

Dugongs and manatees, frequently referred to as sea cows, are also mammals that bear their live young in the water. Dugongs have a single offspring, born underwater, which is pushed to the surface for air. Manatees are affectionate at any time. At mating season, they are particularly so, with the pair nuzzling and embracing frequently. There result from this union, one or two calves which are fed underwater in a horizontal position.

The shark shown above has just given birth to live young. In a few moments these young fish will be actively swimming through the water, small replicas of their parents.

Most mammals give live birth on land to well-developed offspring. Child care among baboons, for example (right), is prolonged until the young are almost fully mature and able to care for themselves. The opossum baby seen below is just crawling into its mother's pouch where it will remain, attached to her nipples, until strong enough to do some independent exploring.

The baby proboscis monkey (below, right) may look grosteque to us, but his mother thinks he is beautiful.

Live Birth on Land. When we speak of live birth on land, we think first of the mammals, for, indeed, these are the dominant land animals. There are, however, amphibians and reptiles that give birth on land to live young.

The advantages of live birth over eggs are obvious. When the young emerge from the mother as fully developed new life, they are safer from the elements as well as from predators than they would be housed in eggs.

One species of salamander, which makes its home in the Alps, has its live young there in the melting snows.

Some lizards and snakes also have live young. Viper babies, carried within the mother's body until they hatch from their eggs, already have enough venom in their fangs to kill several rodents. Cottonmouths and copper-

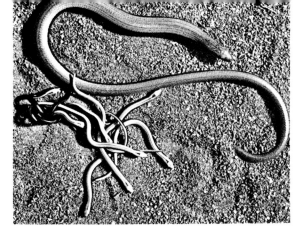

heads are also live-bearers, as are sea snakes, which come to small crevices in the rocks on near-by islands to bear their young.

But, really, it is the mammals that have perfected the business of live birth on land. Through the possession of a special structure known as a placenta, mother mammals are enabled to feed their young internally until they are fairly mature. Blood passes from the mother to the embryo through the placenta. Although mammals have perfected this system, other animals—such as some of the fish and reptiles we have discussed—have modified placentas.

Two groups of mammals do not have placentas. Members of one of these, the monotremes, lay eggs. The others, the marsupials, have young at a very immature stage, which are then carried in pouches covering the mother's nipples.

Mammals, generally do not have elaborate courting rituals. Smaller mammals make nests, but with nothing like the versatility one finds in birds.

The reproductive area in which the mammals truly excel is in child care after birth.

Land animals of many ways of life give birth. Although most reptiles lay eggs, there are live-bearing snakes, like this one. Seals come hundreds of miles to well-established breeding areas on land. The baby rabbits and newborn colt look pretty helpless now, but in short while they will be on their legs and ready for life.

The young lizard sitting on the adult's head is probably just there by accident, for most lizards are quite indifferent to their offspring, expecting them to fend for themselves.

Alligators, on the other hand, although pretty ferocious with other animals, sometimes make excellent mothers. They build mound nests which protect the developing eggs, spend a great deal of time in the area, and come at the call of the young to help extricate them after hatching.

Caring for the Young

Most fish do not spend a great deal of time caring for their young. The usual method is to lay thousands of eggs, then swim away and forget about them. Because of the large number of eggs, some are bound to survive. If all did, there would be an overpopulation problem in the seas. There are, however, several notable exceptions.

Several species, including such popular aquarium pets as cichlids and also certain catfish, are mouth-breeders. Eggs are picked up by either male or female and held in the mouth until hatched. This parent does not eat for the entire duration of incubation. Once hatched, the young may return to the mouth they call home until they become too large to fit into it.

Other fascinating aquarium fish, like the betas and guaramis, make bubble nests for their eggs. The male produces the bubbles with muceus from his mouth combined with air and water and this mass floats to the surface. It is also the male who places the fertilized eggs in the nest and guards and repairs it afterwards.

Male sea horses carry their young in a pouch on their underside. At the proper moment, the father wraps his tail around a plant and with muscular spasms similar to labor contractions, ejects the perfectly formed babies, one at a time, into the water.

There are many other examples of child

care among the fishes, but all of these are exceptions to the general rule of indifference.

Amphibians are also likely to ignore the eggs they have laid. Once again, this is because of the large number of eggs deposited. Where there are fewer eggs, more attention is paid to their preservation.

In midwife toads, it is the male who cares for the eggs. He wraps the long string taken from his mate around his hind thighs and thereafter cares for the eggs, carrying them with him as he feeds and bathes.

Certain female treefrogs have a pouch on the back which the male helpfully stuffs with her eggs, once they are fertilized. When the tadpoles have hatched, the female reaches up with her hind foot and carefully opens the slit of the pouch, so the delicate larvae can escape.

Reptile parents, like fish and amphibians, are not overly devoted to their offspring. Turtles ignore their eggs completely, as do most lizards. However, the green lizard of Europe stays near her eggs until they hatch. Female skinks are very maternal, turning their eggs and wrapping themselves around their clutch. In some species the mother even stays with the hatched young cleaning them regularly.

Baby crocodiles begin to croak as they hatch out of their eggs, and the mother croc returns to help them from the nest mound that she had constructed earlier.

Even in the rare instances of parental care

Most birds are devoted parents. Much back-breaking labor is required to satisfy the insatiable appetites of their young (above), and hundreds of trips are made daily to procure the bits of food necessary to sustain them. Baby birds are, in addition, very vulnerable and must be guarded from predators. Even after they have matured some-what, a careful watch must be kept, and some bird parents have to enforce strict discipline (below) to keep their energetic youngsters in line.

Compared to the labor of gathering food for the young (opposite page), the suckling ability developed by mammals was a great step forward in animal evolution. The many varieties which nurture their babies with milk from their own bodies range from wild pigs like the peccary (top) and hoofed mammals like the zebra (right) to such strange creatures as the scaly pangolin below, whose young here is not nursing but hitching a ride on its mother's tail.

among certain fish, amphibians, and reptiles, it is never of very long duration. Birds have extended this duty into a long labor of love, beginning with the elaborate nest and ending with the fully fledged offspring. In some instances, only the mother cares for the young, but some species have both parents doing heavy duty.

Such birds as fowl, ducks, and ostriches are well feathered and able to leave the nest at birth. The ostrich father manages, in spite of his large harem and subsequent large numbers of offspring, to keep all the chicks in order and protect them against their enemies.

Female ducks bear the entire burden of child-raising, bustling in front of the brood as they are led to and from the water.

Male and female geese and swans mate for life and care for their families jointly. Swan parents keep their babies with them for a year, frequently nestling them on their backs between their uplifted wings.

Song birds, pigeons, and birds of prey are all born naked and helpless. It takes weeks of careful nurturing before they are ready to leave the nest. Feeding goes on continuously, and vigilance against predators must be constant. In many cases the parents will deliberately attract the attention of enemies to lead them away from the nest.

Mammals take their parental responsibilities so seriously that they not only care for

their young until they are almost mature, but feed them with milk from their own bodies. Even the peculiar egg-laying monotremes have special milk-producing glands for feeding after the young have hatched. Mammal milk is a complete food, containing protein, fat, sugar, and salt. The nursing time varies in the various species from a few weeks in a rodent to six months in a whale. Mammal mothers stand, sit, or lie down while nursing, depending on the location of the teats. In some, like deer and horses, they are located toward the back; apes and bats have them on the chest; cats and dogs have teats almost the whole length of the belly.

Among the pouched mammals, nursing is particularly important. Marsupial babies are born at a very immature stage. Opossum babies, for instance, are tiny and have only the use of the front legs. They manage to wriggle up to the mother's pouch, where each grasps a nipple in its mouth. The nipple then expands and the baby is permanently attached until sufficiently mature to venture out into the world.

In placental mammals, the time spent in nursing is proportionately shorter than among marsupials, but still very important. Suckling is not constant but takes place at regular intervals.

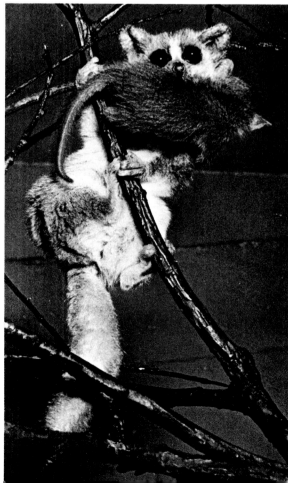

Sometimes when the mother colugo goes flapping off to find food, she leaves her baby at home in its tree nest. But there are occasions when he must be taken along and then it is up to him to hang on tight to mother's belly fur or nipples as she glides rapidly from tree to tree.

Female bats sometimes hibernate together in large clusters throughout the cold weather. They wake together on the first warm day and simultaneous labor takes place, each mother bearing one child. These are naked and blind and cling to their mothers' stomachs, head downward, during flight.

The offspring of the plant-eaters learn rather quickly to take advantage of the abundant food at their disposal, but young hunters have a more difficult time learning their trade. Frequently, adult hunters bring meat to their young and spend weeks in teaching them how to hunt.

The group in which the greatest degree of family life is practiced is that of the primates. In these animals, parental care is long-enduring and several generations may go on living together in harmony. It has been said that the largest reason for man's domination of the world is the very long care and protection given the young by their parents.

Movement

In contrast to plants, animals generally get about. They move from place to place in their search for food and in their avoidance of enemies. Even in those instances where the animal is sessile, or attached, it will agitate its immediate environment by means of tentacles or other structures in order to provide itself with nourishment.

Vertebrates, particularly, excel in many kinds of locomotion; they are propelled by the power of body and limb musculature to fly like

The swimming power of fins is well demonstrated by these catfish (right). The muscular tail and its fin work like a propeller, the paired side fins are for steering and balance, and the unpaired fins along the back and underside prevent it from tilting sideways. The highly sensitive barbels around the mouth and head of catfish help in orientation and food-gathering.

The sea turtle (top) instead of using body movement for swimming utilizes its flipper limbs. These are built like paddles and the turtle literally rows itself along. In order to lighten their weight, sea turtles have less bone than other turtles underneath the bony top layer of shell.

eagles, crawl like snakes, gallop like horses, waddle like ducks, or leap like porpoises.

Forms of locomotion vary from movement through water to movement on and above ground; from subterranean tunneling to tree-climbing, gliding, and true flight.

Swimming. All vertebrates can swim to a degree if they have to—an ability built into the fish-descended vertebrate body. But, of course, this ability varies from group to group, depending on the degree of aquatic involvement. Whales and porpoises can swim as well and in some respects better than fish, whereas a horse or dog, or a human being, will swim only when special occasion demands.

Because of the construction of the vertebral column and the muscles attached to it, most vertebrates, including secondary swimmers, like crocodiles and salamanders, when they swim use various side-to-side movements of the body. If the tail is involved as a propulsive organ, it is generally flattened from side to side like the fish tail. In fish, the tail is the main driving force and works on the principle of the screw propeller. The same technique is in effect among those torpedo-shaped aquatic mammals, the whales and dolphins, except that here the movements of the body are up and down, with the tail flukes correspondingly flattened in the horizontal plane—that is the tailfin extends from side to side, to provide a propellerlike thrust.

The bottle-nosed dolphin, like all members of the whale group, has a fish-shaped body. It uses its muscular tail and horizontal tail flukes as a propeller, the fin-shaped front limbs serving for steering and balance.

Aquatic birds and mammals have developed their own solutions to swimming. Waterfowl propel themselves by means of powerful strokes of their webbed feet. The middle photograph shows a graylag goose "shipping oars" between strokes. Penguins (bottom), on the other hand, have converted their wings to efficient, oarlike flippers, and use their hind legs only for steering.

81

Other aquatic vertebrates displace water not by means of a screw-propeller tail but by using the principle of the oar or paddle. The limbs are used alternately or together for rowing the body through water. Here the anatomical adaptive change consists in varying degrees of conversion from a land foot to a broad, flat surface. This is accomplished either by way of webbing between otherwise fairly "regular" toes, or by way of more deep-seated changes in the bony structure of the foot, converting it to a finlike flipper. Among these paddlers can be numbered aquatic birds, such as penguins and auks, which use their flipper-like wings. It is interesting to note that already among the very early birds during the latter part of the Age of Dinosaurs, a similar adaptation to aquatic life had taken place. The primitive bird *Hesperornis* had the same kind of wings as auks have today. Ducks, geese, and swans, of course, use their webbed feet for paddling.

Many marine reptiles, particularly the turtles, have perfected rowing techniques. Sea turtles use both front and back flippers, with the latter also serving for balance and ruddering. The fresh-water and pond turtles have webbed feet which they use very effectively as they chase water insects and small fish. In past ages, there were the paddle-limbed marine plesiosaurs, oarsmen par excellence. They shared the seas with the ichthyosaurs, marine reptiles which, instead of rowing, preceded the aquatic mammals (dolphins and whales) in the evolution of a fishlike body and propelling tailfin. Again, as with fish fins, the finlike limbs of dolphins and ichthyosaurs serve mainly for steering and balance.

Among mammals, the rowers include the web-footed duckbilled platypus and the flippered seals. Sea lions and fur seals use both front and back flippers for land movement, but in the water propel themselves with their front flippers alone, the back pair being used for steering only. The hair seals on the other hand, use mainly their hind flippers for paddling, their front flippers being the only pair in use when they are moving on land. Webbed hind feet are used by beavers, who also own a flattened tail that serves mainly for balance, but which is also occasionally used as an up-and-down scull.

River otters (above) use various body movements and the thrust of a long, muscular tail for swimming.

Among the cartilaginous fishes, the bottom-dwelling rays (below) have wing-shaped pectoral fins that undulate gracefully as they help drive their owner across the sea floor, with the whipping tail supplying force from behind. Three paddlers are shown on the opposite page. The extinct reptilian plesiosaurs (top) were remarkable "oarsmen" with large rowing limbs. Pond turtles (opposite page, bottom left) use their webbed fore and hind feet in an alternating paddling rhythm. When swimming, the beaver (opposite page, right) uses powerful strokes of its webbed hind feet, with the flattened tail serving mainly for balance.

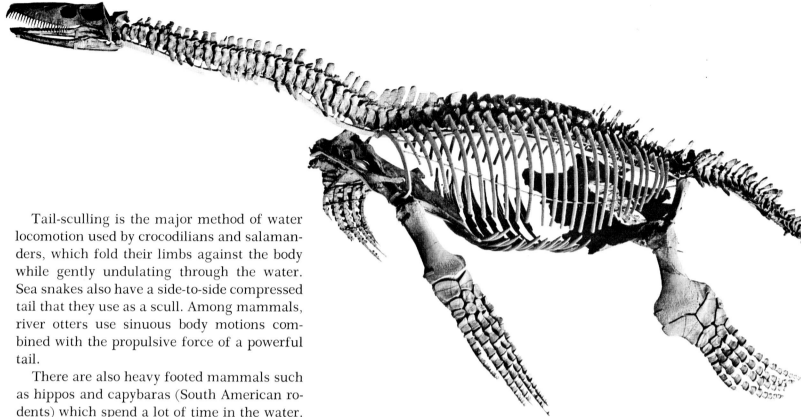

Tail-sculling is the major method of water locomotion used by crocodilians and salamanders, which fold their limbs against the body while gently undulating through the water. Sea snakes also have a side-to-side compressed tail that they use as a scull. Among mammals, river otters use sinuous body motions combined with the propulsive force of a powerful tail.

There are also heavy footed mammals such as hippos and capybaras (South American rodents) which spend a lot of time in the water. These use a rather clumsy dog paddle when swimming.

Crawling and Walking. When the first amphibian crawled on land, it did just that—it crawled. Although now in possession of terrestrial limbs instead of fins, amphibians such as salamanders hardly raise the body off the ground. The sprawled-out legs serve as props against the soil, and body movement is still in terms of the fish S-shaped curve now transmitted as a shouldering and hip-thrusting movement that throws one leg forward at a time. In that fashion the body is always propped up by at least three legs forming a tripod of support over the animal's center of gravity. The basic sequence of limb movement is always the same, and it is always at a diagonal across the body. The four legs are lifted from the ground (or replaced on the ground) in a definite order. If we begin to watch when the right forefoot lifts, the next leg raised is always the left rear; this is followed by the left forelimb, and this in turn by the hind leg on the right side. A crawling baby moves in exactly the same way and the basic walking pattern of all four-legged vertebrates follows this diagonal sequence.

Reptiles possess the same kind of sprawling "akimbo" limbs as do amphibians, but many of them can raise their bodies well off the ground—at least for short periods of time. This can be observed in lizards and even the slow-moving land turtles.

The most primitive kind of four-legged movement on land is practiced by salamanders (above). In these amphibians, motion is derived mainly by way of the segmental body musculature. The S-shaped, belly-on-the-ground posture is typical, and the small limbs "akimbo" to the body serve as alternately placed props when the animal crawls forward.

Being a lizard, this monitor (middle) has the characteristic sprawled-out reptilian limb position. However, as we see here, the body can on occasion be raised well off the ground.

Turtles, too, have limbs directed outward at an angle from the body (bottom). However, in spite of its awkward appearance, the pond turtle can move surprisingly quickly on land.

Like all snakes, the Old World water snake (shown on the opposite page) moves by throwing its body into loops. Forward motion is accomplished by pushing and then straightening the loops against the ground. Snakes can always gain traction since the ground is never completely even.

Among reptiles, snakes, as legless descendants of burrowing lizards, present a special case. By throwing the body into S-shaped curves, contact is made with irregularities of the surface, against which snakes push—the result is forward movement. A snake is practically helpless on a completely smooth surface. Some snakes possess big belly scales that can be moved by special muscles to help in locomotion. In a narrow tunnel kind of situation, when the snake cannot loop sideways, it moves forward like an inchworm, shortening and straightening out its body in what is called the "concertina" movement.

The extinct mammal-like reptiles developed, along with many other mammalian characters, a stance in which the legs were drawn in under the body, with the elbows facing

backward and the knees forward. Most mammals now possess this kind of limb orientation.

The walk of mammals follows the diagonally sequential limb movement already outlined. (There are a few exceptions: elephants, giraffes, camels, and hyenas frequently move both legs on the same side in a gait called pacing which gives those animals a side-to-side rolling kind of walk.) Mammals have also developed specialized movements for rapid locomotion. In a walk, a quadruped (four-legged animal) is always supported by three limbs and can stop in its tracks without falling over. When it speeds up, however, the next limb in the sequence is lifted before the previous one reaches the ground and there is a moment when only two diagonally opposite feet are on the ground. This gait is called a

limbs impart all the propulsive power and the back muscles play a minor role. This, then, is quite different from the method of fishes, amphibians and reptiles, where side-to-side movements of the back are the main source of moving power. However, many mammals do use the power of the back musculature in locomotion. A galloping greyhound, for instance, arches and stretches its body to increase the force and length of its stride. But here the contractions are in the vertical or up-and-down rather than the horizontal or side-to-side plane.

There are quite a few vertebrates that use a bipedal or two-legged walk rather than a four-legged one. The whole class of birds are bipedal, since the forefeet are now adapted for flight. Birds have accordingly worked out a

Although considerably more graceful, antelopes (opposite page) share with rhinoceroses the basic mammalian pattern and posture of four-footed walking. Bears, however, often stand upright on their hind legs (below).

The lesser panda (below, left) walks by placing the whole sole of each foot on the ground.

The Indian black-necked stork (bottom, left) demonstrates to an almost exaggerated extent the placement of legs typical for birds when walking.

trot, and the resulting lack of stability is counterbalanced by the rapid placement of feet.

Only a few mammals are capable of a true gallop, the most noteworthy being the horse, where only one foot touches the ground at any time, and there are even momentary periods when all the feet are in midair. In the case of a galloping horse, the muscles that move the

Horses (above) are perfectly equipped for rapid movement over dry ground. Their hoofs are actually the tips of what would be the middle toes and fingers in other vertebrates, enormously enlarged at the expense of having lost all the other digits.

The kangaroo balances its weight on a tripod formed by the tail and the elongated hind limbs (below). During the jump, the tail serves as a counterbalance.

center of gravity for their bodies that is directly in line with their hind feet rather than toward the middle of the body. Their walking legs, too, are directly beneath the body and they walk with their heels well off the ground.

Walking on the toes (called digitigrade movement) is also practiced by many fast moving mammals, notably the horse which actually stands on tip of the middle toe (its hoof), all the other toes having disappeared in the course of evolution. Dogs and cats, too are digitigrade when they run, but their carnivore relatives, the bears, are plantigrade, meaning that they walk flat-footed with heels or wrists on the ground.

Man is the only tailless animal that ordinarily walks on two legs. Apes can walk erect without their hands touching the ground, but only for very short periods. Bears, too, can move bipedally on occasion. A different sort of hind-end balance has been achieved by the long-tailed jumpers. Here the tail is used as a third prop or for counterbalance. Leaping mammals such as kangaroos (marsupials), jerboas, and kangaroo rats (both rodents) propel themselves with power from the long hind

legs. During the jump (which in some kangaroos can cover 25 feet) the air-borne tail serves as a counterweight; during hopping, the tail becomes a third prop. Among reptiles, some lizards, when in a hurry, can run on their hind legs, using long tails for counterbalance. And many of the dinosaurs, too, were bipedal, especially the flesh-eaters, some of which had

almost grotesquely small forelimbs in proportion to their huge hind legs and heavy tail.

The frogs, among the amphibians, have relinquished their tails, in the process of developing powerful hind legs used for both swimming and jumping. Both frogs and toads hop, but toads also progress by the more ordinary vertebrate diagonal walking gait.

One does not ordinarily think of fish as walking but there are several kinds that have modified fins that they can use for propping themselves against the bottom as they undulate forward.

It might be interesting to look at some top speeds of land animals. The cheetah holds the record at 70 m.p.h.; next would be some of the gazelles, capable of moving around 60 m.p.h. A running man can hit 20 m p.h., but he doubles his capacity when mounted on a galloping horse. As an equestrian he is neck-to-neck with running ostriches, leaping hares, and galloping foxes. Some snakes can actually approach 10 m.p.h. on a short dash and a wild pig can manage 30 m.p.h., which seems to be about average for many animals: the smaller cats, bison, giraffes, moose, bighorn sheep, and even on occasion the cumbersome rhinoceros.

The giraffe shown here is going all out, reaching 30 m.p.h. Giraffes use a gait called pacing, where both legs are used on the same side at the same time. This makes the body rock from side to side.

Ostriches use enormous strides when in a hurry, literally leaping along as they attain a speed (approximately 50 m.p.h.) exceeding that of a galloping horse.

Although somewhat awkward in appearance (below), gnus share with other antelopes the ability to move at a 50 m.p.h. gallop.

Digging and Burrowing. It is frequently of advantage to get underground to avoid enemies or temperature extremes on the surface; also ants, termites, beetle grubs, earthworms, and plant roots to be found there can provide nourishment. Even domestic dogs frequently dig holes in which to bury bones, and pigs root with their snouts to get at underground plant food. However, there are representatives from all the classes of vertebrates that have specialized in a fossorial, or burrowing, way of life. Among mammals, moles are probably the best known diggers. Their forelimbs have undergone anatomical changes that make them effective "shovels" in the rapid excavation of long underground mazes in which they spend their lives. There is also a pouched mole in Australia that lives very much the same way, and several rodents have also gone in for a molelike way of life. These full-time burrowers have greatly reduced vision, the main emphasis being on the senses of touch and smell.

Among the part-time burrowers can be numbered many desert rodents (for example, kangaroo rats) who spend the major portion of the day underground and come out at dusk to gather food.

As ungainly as it may seem when walking (top), the aardvark is a veritable bulldozer when it comes to digging.

In all moles (right), smell is the dominant sense; the eyes are tiny and there are no outer ears.

Another form of burrower, a troop of spiny anteaters or echidnas is shown at far right rooting and digging for ants.

Many ant- and termite-eaters have developed sharp digging foreclaws for the opening up of underground nests. The South American ant-eaters share this characteristic with the spiny ant-eater of Australia and New Guinea. The latter also lives in burrows that it excavates, and when frightened literally digs itself into the ground. The African aardvark is another kind of ant- and termite-eating mammal that digs superbly, and spends most of the day in its cool underground den. Many mammals will dig out dens in which to live or raise their young and among them the badger excels as a subterranean engineer.

Reptiles can count quite a few burrowers among their ranks. Many snakes live underground, at least for part of the time, and there are also a number of limbless lizards that have specialized in a fossorial existence. These all use their blunt heads as a digging tool. Desert tortoises dig deep tunnels into the dry ground with shovel-shaped forearms. These underground havens are then frequently shared with certain frogs and other desert dwellers.

Among the amphibians, spade-foot toads have earned their name because of a sharp cutting edge on the side of each hind foot that enables them to dig under. And the peculiar earthworm-shaped caecilians are a whole group of amphibians that live an entirely underground existence.

Certain fish, too, for example the slender elongated pipefish, a relative of the seahorses, spend a great deal of time buried up to their gills in the sand on the bottom of their watery environment.

The kangaroo rat of the Southwestern American desert spends the day in a cool burrow and only comes out at dusk to feed. It never drinks and can produce water internally from the seeds it eats.

Climbing.

Another way of avoiding unpleasantness on the surface of the ground is to get up into bushes or trees. The arboreal habitat offers many food items in the form of insect life and plant products (leaves and fruit).

Mostly, arboreal locomotion is a special case of the standard terrestrial walking and running movement. Added to this are grasping devices that prevent falling. Among mammals, grasping hands and feet are particularly characteristic of monkeys, but are also possessed by opossums and certain mice. A prehensile tail—a terminal appendage that can be wrapped around branches—also helps when the animal is high above the ground. South American monkeys, porcupines, arboreal anteaters and many Australian tree-climbing marsupials have this kind of a device. Tree sloths use sharp, curved claws as grappling hooks with which to move in an upside-down position.

The grasping foot and prehensile tail also figure among reptiles—the Old World chameleon being the best example. Other lizards (e.g. geckos) have developed specialized toepads that permit hanging on to almost completely smooth surfaces, as they chase insects up and down rocks or walls. A suction-disc kind of toe is a characteristic of tree frogs. It is also a development on the hands and feet of certain primitive primates, the tarsiers— an example of how similar adaptive solutions to a problem are frequently worked out independently by different animals.

The tarsier (opposite page) is a hopper on the branches of trees. Its fingers and toes have suction-cup tips, a big help when holding on.

The scaly mammal called a pangolin (top left) is inching its way up a straight trunk. Heavy claws serve as grappling hooks.

The Old World chameleon (center) has two obvious anatomical features keyed to climbing: its "wrap-around" tail, and the toes arranged like a big pincer.

The tree frog (bottom left) is quite similar to the tarsier in its climbing adaptations.

The koala bear (below), an Australian marsupial, has its fingers and toes arranged very much like those of the chameleon.

The flying squirrel is not really a flier—it glides from heights, using a membrane of skin stretched between front and hind limbs as a sort of parachute.

Gliding. There are quite a few vertebrates that have added gliding to the repertory of movement in trees. Many arboreal vertebrates leap from branch to branch, being in free fall part of time. Hence, any anatomical change that increases spread-out surface on the principle of a parachute, is of adaptive advantage in maneuvering.

Among mammals, the best gliders are flying squirrels, flying phalangers (a kind of Australian marsupial) and the so-called "flying lemurs," or colugos. All these have a membrane of skin extending from the sides of the body and also attached to the hind and front limbs. Thus, with legs spread and often with fluffy tails acting as controls, these mammals can glide considerable distances between trees and branches or to the ground.

Some lizards also have gliding membranes that can be extended like wings by way of elongated ribs along the sides of the body. Certain tree snakes have greatly flattened bodies that act as parachutes during glides. And even the frogs can number gliders in their ranks—certain Asiatic tree frogs that extend the webbing between their long hind toes.

True Flight.
The step from passive gliding to flying is a major one and not too many vertebrates have succeeded in this engineering feat. One whole class of vertebrates, however, is distinguished by its ability to stay aloft, through the active beating of wings displacing air.

Reptiles of past ages experimented with flight several times—once as pterosaurs and then in the form of birds. The latter have been tremendously successful, but the pterosaurs enjoyed only a temporary conquest. Pterosaurs used a thin membrane extending from the top of a greatly elongated fourth finger to the hind legs, and they were essentially passive gliders rather than true fliers. There were many kinds, some no bigger than sparrows, others with

This extinct "flying" reptile (below) was one of the large pterosaurs, cousins to the birds. Pterosaurs were mostly gliders, using their leathery wing membranes extended from enormously elongated fourth fingers.

The screech owl (bottom left) nicely demonstrates the down-stroke wing position during the flapping cycle. Note how the wing tips almost meet in front of the head.

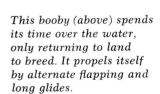

This booby (above) spends its time over the water, only returning to land to breed. It propels itself by alternate flapping and long glides.

95

25-foot wingspreads, but they all gave way when that feathered reptile, the bird, began its active flapping of wings.

Birds, of course, also use simple gliding techniques during flight. Some, like shearwaters and albatrosses can glide low over the water for miles with barely a wingbeat. And eagles and vultures can soar for long distances at great heights.

When a bird beats its wings upwards and downward, it provides a lifting force for itself that is equal to the weight of its body, and a forward thrust equal to the backward drag of the air. Rather than comparing a bird with an airplane, a better analogy would be the helicopter: the rotor and screw-blade being the equivalent of the flapping wings. Control in flight is achieved by using the tail feathers as a horizontal rudder, and partly by changing the shape and posture of the wings. It seems that the downward stroke of the wing, brought about by the very heavy musculature attached to the birds keeled breastbone, is the main propulsive agent during active flight. The down stroke begins with the wings fully extended, stretched up over the back of the bird. Both wings then stroke downward and forward to meet in front of the body. The backward and upward stroke that now follows first uncovers the head of the bird, and then draws the wing back and up in position for a new downward stroke.

Besides birds, only the bats have mastered true flight. They utilize a membrane of skin stretched between three or four fingers, the sides of the body and the hind legs.

Talons extended and coming in for the kill (opposite page), the powerful hawk is braking with its outstretched wings and tail. Despite the snake's all-out desperate dash, it really doesn't have a chance against this bombardier from on high.

Like all bats, this pipestrelle (below) flies just like a bird, using a similiar sequence of actively beating wing movement. The wings, however, are naked membranes of skin, extended between several fingers, the sides of the body, and the hind legs.

Every creature in nature must have some means of protecting itself. The tuatara (right) of New Zealand not only blends very well with the surroundings, but digs well and hides in burrows in times of danger.

The green toad (below), like most of his family, has spotted skin covered with splotches of mud and dust to make him appear a part of the scenery.

Protection

Even when one has been extraordinarily successful at developing means of feeding, reproducing, and movement in this world of dog-eat-dog, it all goes for nothing if one is vulnerable to attack. Unless one can defend oneself against the enemy, the end is near. For this reason, every animal has developed some means of protection, worked out in conjunction with the individual's way of life.

Sometimes the defense is passive and individual; sometimes it involves the cooperation of a large group; for some the best defense is offense. In each case, wariness is of utmost importance. Every animal must be aware of ever-present danger from enemies if he is not to be a "goner." In those groups in which great self-confidence made its members lose track of this great rule, the results have been disastrous. Great cats, like the tigers, which felt themselves invulnerable because of their great strength, have been hunted almost to extinction by man, the most thoughtless killer ever to have walked the earth. The same holds true for such groups as elephants, eagles, rhinoceroses, and bison. Smaller animals, who have always had to be alert to danger, have been more successful in continuing the almost futile effort of holding their own in this man-dominated environment.

But, after all, in the total history of nature, man's stay on earth is of very recent origin and some animals are beginning to learn how to cope with him. Given enough time, they may yet be able to find means of holding on. Coyotes, for instance, have made a great comeback and are occupying territory they had not held in the past. There is hope for nature.

The leopard's use of camouflage is primarily offensive rather than defensive. With the dappled skin rendering him indiscernible from the rest of the environment, his victims are unaware of his presence until too late.

The rattlesnake (above) employs the rattle as a warning device, more for its own sake than in respect to the approching intruders. Large animals that could not possibly be captured and eaten by a rattler can still be injured by its poison. So, when the warning sound is heard, the snake is given a wide berth by everyone in the neighborhood. This saves the rattlesnake from being stepped on by large clumsy creatures like cattle and men.

The Australian leaf-tailed gecko (top right) has camouflage in the shape of its tail as well as in its color.

Camouflage and Warning Signals. All the various means of defense developed by animals have been copied by mankind for use against one another. One of the most popular has been camouflage. In the animal kingdom camouflage has been used passively, as in the birds, in order to hide from one's enemies and aggressively, as in the leopards, who remain in ambush until exactly the right moment for the kill. Some animals combine both motives, like lizards, for instance, who hide from enemies while waiting inconspicuously for insects.

Camouflage usually has to do with color. Protective coloration involves blending in so perfectly with one's surroundings that one cannot be seen. Lizards have a remarkable ability to change their color to correspond with the immediate surroundings. Old World chameleons are the absolute masters of camouflage. Their skin contains star-shaped color cells of black, yellow, red, and white. These cells contain grains of pigment which contract and expand in response to stimulation from the nerves. As one color expands, the other contracts, allowing the chameleons to change quickly from black to red, for instance, as the occasion demands. If both red and yellow expand simultaneously, the resulting coloration will be orange.

But most animals have to be content with just one pattern of coloration, tying in with one environmental situation. They will, therefore, spend the majority of their time in that situation in which they feel protected and venture into other surroundings only at times of least danger. Young deer, for instance, are spotted to blend with the sun-dappled forest in which they spend their days. It is only during the evening, when visibility is lessened, that they will carefully set out into the meadows to feed.

Each class of animals has those that rely upon camouflage for protection. There are fish living near the bottom of the sea that blend with the coral or the sand. Fresh-water bottom-dwellers look like rocks. There are frogs and toads that are dappled to blend with the moist, swamp areas they inhabit; salamanders that look like rocks or earth; snakes like grass or leaves. Bob whites are colored to be inconspicuous in high grass, and weasels are earth-colored in the summer and snow-colored in the winter.

Some animals have found that their best defense is in looking dangerous. These animals do not blend with their surroundings, but stand out starkly against them. Such animals are sometimes poisonous and the rest of the animal world has learned to associate brilliant colors with danger. Therefore, several other, quite harmless creatures, have adopted bright-red or yellow coloring to frighten off potential enemies. In any case, the warning is carefully respected. Very few will closely approach the brightly colored coral snake, and only a fool would overlook the striking black-and-white contrast characteristic of a skunk.

One method of camouflage other than the use of color is to take on initiative or startling shapes. There are, for instance, chameleons that look like dried leaves and geckos that resemble bark. Many lizards have frills or collars that they can extend to appear ferocious and even frogs may blow out facial pouches to seem bigger. Some snakes have tails that are shaped like heads to confuse their enemies into attacking the wrong end.

The green mamba has two very effective weapons at its disposal. The first and obvious one, as seen at left, is the protective coloring of this arboreal snake. The second is an extremely virulent poison.

All larks (center) nest on the ground, and the protective coloring they wear is extremely important to their survival.

Fish, too, frequently blend with their surroundings. This fish (bottom) can scarcely be distinguished from the rocks.

Members of the rockfish, or scorpion fish, group have fin spines to protect them. Turkey fish like the one below have venom glands attached to the spines, making them even more effective.

Armor and Spines. Another effective animal technique of resistance is the use of heavy plating to protect the vulnerable parts of the body.

A turtle is sort of a walking tank. It plods slowly along, justifiably confident that nothing can harm it. Its back and underside are completely covered with a shield of fused, bony plates. In case of real emergency, there are openings large enough for complete withdrawal of head, arms, legs, and tail. This arrangement is complex and unique to the turtle, and the anatomical adaptations that have made this defense possible are wondrous, indeed. The ribs of these reptiles have grown outward to cover the bony girdles to which the

limbs attach and support the top shell, or carapace. The bottom shell, or plastron, connects to the carapace along the sides, and the whole shell is covered with hornlike plates.

The armor of the armadillo is different, but just as effective. Over the shoulders and hips, there are solid bony shields between which are movable bands of armor that offers flexibility as well as protection. There is also armor on the head and tail. If danger seems imminent, the armadillo can avail himself of the flexibility of his back to roll into a tight ball in which his vulnerable underparts are completely hidden.

Some animals have developed sharp spines as a kind of armor. Burrfish are also called "balloonfish" and "porcupine fish." All three names are apt, for these creatures have hollow spines that normally lie against the body but that stand out straight when these fish inflate themselves into veritable balloons of air.

Porcupines, too, have long quills for use against intruders. Normally peace-loving, these rodents are quite able to care for themselves in an emergency. They simply turn their backs, raise and vibrate their quills, and wait. If the threat is not immediately removed, the porcupine runs backward and spears the interloper unmercifully.

The Mediterranean land turtle (top) and the banded armadillos of the United States (bottom) both wear armor, but of different sorts. The turtle's shell is a solid shield of fused bony plates, with openings large enough to accommodate the head and legs in time of danger when complete withdrawal is desirable. The armadillo's armor consists of solid shields over shoulders and hips, with movable bands of armor between, offering more flexibility to the body. As the head and the tail are also armored, the animal can protect all the soft underparts by rolling up in a ball.

The Old World porcupine (left) is covered with stout cylindrical quills. When threatened, this rodent erects its quills, turns its back on the intruder, and stands ready to defend itself.

The male duck-billed platypus has a poisonous spur in his hind foot, which is used, not for defense, but to subdue the female while mating. The venomous fangs of a viper (lower right), of which the rattlesnake is an example, bend inward when the mouth is closed. When the snake is ready to strike, the jaws open wide and the fangs are in killing position.

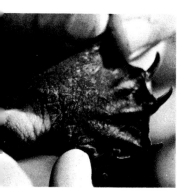

Poison. There are several types of animals whose mastery in the use of poison makes the Borgias look like sissies. Animals, however, unlike humans, use this substance only for self-defense or to help in acquiring food. Indeed, many animals which need their poison-killing facility to keep them supplied with food, hesitate to use it for protection and give ample warning to approaching intruders.

Scorpion fish, however, use their poison only for protection. These odd-looking creatures that hover on the bottom of shallow seas have strong, elongated spines located around the head and fins. Beneath each spine is a poison gland, and a hollow groove runs through from the gland to the tip of the spine. Any pressure against the tip causes the gland to eject its venom into the puncture made by the spine. The poisonous jab of some species can kill a human, that of other species may paralyze; the best that can be expected is intense pain.

Stingrays are almost as ominous as they look. Their undulating, wide-winged pectoral fins allow them to skim with seeming effortlessness across the bottom of the sea. From the top surface of the whiplike tail, about three-quarters of the way down, project one or two flattened spines.

Beneath the spine are venom glands. When the stingray is aroused, it can whip its flexible spine-bearing tail about in several directions and strike with astonishing force any being it considers a foe. As stingrays count on their swimming ability and sharp teeth to procure the food they need, the terrifying tail is used solely for protection.

Many amphibians have a little poison in their skins. In most, it is barely enough to discourage the small mammals which usually prey upon them. One group, however, is known as the "arrow poison" frogs, for the South American Indians have found the venom secreted by these amphibians to be fatally effective in hunting small game.

No poison is as highly feared as that possessed by the venomous snakes. Engendering this fear is the threatening posture of the snake or the warning sound it makes. Snakes, however, use their poison to procure food and are loathe to waste it in defense. It takes severe provocation to make a snake strike. Rattlesnakes and adders have poison that attacks the blood system of their victims, while that of the cobras affects the nervous system. The poison is located in modified salivary glands, and gets ejected through canals within the biting fangs.

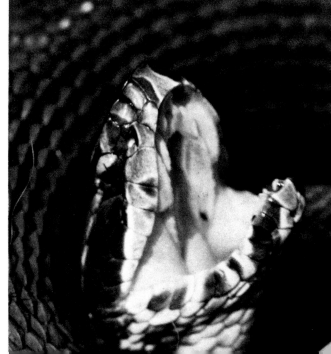

The only poisonous lizards, the gila monster and bearded lizard, have a less efficient poison mechanism, for they have no way of directly injecting the venom. It simply runs along grooves at the front of the regularly-shaped teeth from glands located in the lower jaw.

The egg-laying platypus is peculiar in many respects. Although this mammal has no natural enemies, males have spurs on their ankles connected by narrow canals to poison glands. The poison is used to subdue the female at breeding season, although an over-excited male could kill his mate.

Some species of cobra, like the ringhals shown above, have developed the ability to spit their venom with terrifying accuracy into the eyes of any large animal.

There are only two venomous lizards in the world, of which the Gila monster is one. Unlike most lizards, which are quick moving animals, Gila monsters are sluggish and move slowly. The venom apparatus in these lizards is less efficient than that of the snakes.

Herding and Getting Away Fast.

The idea of safety in numbers is certainly not unique to humans. Many groups of animals operate on the same premise and, in some, the herding technique has been refined to a fine art.

Schools of fish are a familiar sight, even in aquariums, in certain species. There are, in fact, 4,000 species that practice schooling as a daily part of their lives. Schools of fish line up with exact distances between each fish. It is as though an army sergeant were parading his troops—they move and turn with such extraordinary precision. But, oddly enough, there are no leaders; those fish at the front drop back occasionally and a new rank forms. How the schools have managed such perfect discipline is an unknown but undeniably effective protective measure.

Ostriches are extremely gregarious. Not only do they live in large colonies of their own kind, but frequently they are joined by other plains animals such an antelopes and zebras. The association is mutually advantageous, for the mammals flush live food (reptiles and insects) that ostriches enjoy, while the seven foot birds stand guard for the entire gathering.

Although ostriches do not fly, they have no trouble escaping from danger. Living in large groups provides a few members who are always alert to keep guard, and with the ostriches' seven-foot vantage point and keen eyesight, predators are quickly spotted. The speed with which these birds can run when alarmed is equal to or better than that of most enemies.

Pelicans (above) live communally and fly in formation with synchronized wing beats. When the leader spreads its wings to glide, the whole group follows suit.

For a deer, protection is primarily a matter of escape. This one, like most deer, is capable of great speed when the occasion demands.

These marabou storks (right) are gathered together to dine. They will eat frogs, eels, or insects, depending on which they can find. The naked pouch hanging down from the throat is part of the respiratory system.

The birds pictured below left are actually ibises, but are referred to as painted storks. They are highly gregarious and form groups that during nesting may number in the thousands. When in flight, they engage in group gliding.

Shore birds like those at bottom right usually feed together on sea food and nest along the beaches in colonies.

This school of Atlantic mackerel will migrate as a unit from Maine to Chesapeake Bay and back again.

Several methods of dealing with the enemy have been worked out by those who live in herds. In some, the most vigilant members of the group sound the alert and everyone takes to his heels. For others, a defensive position is formed. Musk oxen live in herds numbering up to 100. When they are threatened by the wolves that prey upon them, they form a tight circle with the calves inside, presenting to the enemy a unified rank of ominous horns. This is enough to discourage the wolves, but, unfortunately, it does not work well against men with guns, and many herds have been completely killed off by our great sportsmen.

Other mammals that herd depend upon speed for escape. In giraffe herds, for example, it is the females which keep watch. With their very keen sense of hearing, they are quick to sense danger and give the alarm. The group then immediately takes off with surprising speed for such ungainly looking animals.

The herd animals are not the only ones that count on speed. In fact, if you are an animal without the benefit of protective coloring, poison or armor, your best means of defense is escape, whether your living habits are communal or solitary. This applies to animals in the sea, in the air, and on land. Small fish swim rapidly away from big fish. Frogs and rabbits have long hind legs to carry them in long jumps away from those that are pursuing. In Australia, kangaroos use their powerful legs to hop away from wild dogs and marsupial carnivores. Ducks, when endangered on land, take quickly to the air. Desert lizards scurry quickly through the sand. Deer and antelopes spring rapidly on light feet away from the many meat-eaters that prey upon them. Squirrels scamper wildly through the trees when threatened, as do the monkeys. In each of these groups, the fastest one is the one most likely to survive.

This group of giraffes has come down for a drink of water. They are typical of the species, which usually travel in herds of about fifteen, but sometimes number as many as seventy. In each herd there are an adult male, several females with their calves, and a few adolescent males. The females keep watch and give alarm if danger seems imminent. A giraffe can run about 30 m.p.h. if pressed, but must avoid swampland because its long legs are useless anywhere except on hard ground.

The lamprey at right, which as an adult is a parasite on other fishes, is a degenerate survivor of the first vertebrates, the jawless fishes. Note the holes along the side, behind the eye. These are the external openings of the gill pouches inside. These primitive fishes do not have upper and lower jaws.

These two small sharks are smooth dogfishes from the Mediterranean. Not only do they prey on other fish, but they also feed on marine worms and other invertebrates.

If anything typifies a shark, this specimen of a leopard (also called tiger) shark at bottom fills the bill. Note the triangular fin along the back and the wide-based paired fins on the underside. A powerful and tireless swimmer, the leopard shark hunts fish and marine mammals, but does not disdain collecting garbage at the ocean's bottom.

(opposite) The cartilaginous fishes include not only sharks, but also the skates and rays. Here is a thornback ray clearly showing the undulating movement of the tremendously expanded fins by which these flattened fishes move.

Classification

When one tries to understand the teeming animal world, some method of classifying, of finding relationships, is absolutely necessary. Zoologists have devised a sort of filing system cataloguing the various kinds of animals according to their special characteristics. Within the large category known as vertebrates, there are five major subdvisions called classes—fishes, amphibians, reptiles, birds, and mammals. Each class must be broken down further, for some animals within each class bear more obvious relationships to each other than to others of the same class. Therefore, there are orders, and within each order there are families. Families are broken down still further into genera, and genera into species.

Fishes

Although all the animals we know as fishes bear certain similarities to each other, there are such sharp distinctions among these forms that they are usually considered separately. Hagfishes and lampreys comprise one group, sharks and rays another, and all the bony fishes form the third.

The fossil fish at right is very reminiscent in body shape to living skates and rays. Actually, it is a 400-million-year-old member of an ancient group of fishes with jaws whose relationships to later fishes are not at all clear. The internal skeleton of the fossil was bony and not cartilaginous.

The higher, ray-finned bony fishes, or teleosts, include many diverse subgroups or orders. The brook trout (bottom left) is a typical fish, yet the two snakelike fresh-water eels (bottom right) are just as "fishy." As a group eels are elongated in shape and have lost the rear set of paired fins.

Fishes are the most ancient class of vertebrates, with a history that goes back about 400 million years. In the seas of that eerie, silent period of barren land and empty skies, lived a multitude of invertebrates, some of which slowly began to develop characteristics leading to the vertebrate body. As the vertebrates evolved from fish to amphibian to reptile to bird and mammal, culminating in that most dominant of mammals, man, one group of animals remained in the ocean to remind us of our humble origin.

Lampreys. Humiliating as it may be, the ancestor of all vertebrate life was a creature quite similar to the modern lamprey. Lampreys are naked, eel-like creatures without jaws. In their youth, they live on the bottoms of streams and suck up small animals with disclike, toothless mouths. As they mature and grow teeth, they become parasites, attaching themselves to passing fish into which they then bore a hole, the better to suck the body juices.

Lampreys have a single nostril on top of the head, with eyes on either side. The powerful

An Australian lungfish. This is one of three kinds of lungfishes, survivors from an age when several groups of lobe-finned fishes were common in fresh water. Although the lungfishes were never on the direct ancestral line to amphibians, they share the fleshy structure of the fins possessed by those other lobe-fins that did come on land.

sucker is lined with horny "teeth," which surround the mouth. On the head behind the nose lies a third eye known as the pineal eye. Sea lampreys can grow to be as large as three feet.

The first vertebrates did not go through the parasitic stage, but remained vacuum-cleaner-type feeders that sucked in all the small animal life in their path. They were all jawless without paired fins. The primitive vertebral column had not yet evolved to be the strong, well-articulated structure it was later to be. Many types of jawless fishes evolved, including some with heavy armor and head shields.

A major step in the evolution of vertebrates took place with the appearance of the first jawed fishes. Obviously, an animal equipped with jaws has a much greater range of feeding possibilities than one without. Paired fins, so necessary to expert swimming, also developed.

Armed with well-articulated vertebral columns, snapping jaws, and well-situated fins, the fishes began to take over the seas with extraordinary proficiency. Today there are more than 20,000 species scattered throughout the world. Sharks and rays are divided from the bulk of the species because of their skeletal structure, which is composed of cartilage rather than bone. Both groups, sharks and bony fishes, arose from primitive jawed fishes

at about the same point in history, but the sharks and rays completed their evolution at a very early point, remaining unchanged for millions of years. The bony fishes went on to evolve into thousands of types, adapted to every kind of watery environment.

Sharks and Rays. Modern sharks and rays are mainly marine creatures and can be found in all the seas of the world. Although some reach a length of 40 feet, most species are smaller and some never attain to more than two feet. All sharks and rays are carnivorous, but the rays concentrate primarily on invertebrates found on the bottoms.

Sharks are rather terrifying creatures and one justifiable reason for fearing them is the rows of daggerlike teeth. These teeth are constantly renewed, the worn out ones being replaced by new ones. Within the skin of a shark are other tiny "teeth," sharp closely set pieces of bone that are very abrasive.

Rays are equally ominous in appearance, with their flat, winglike fins extended as they skim silently by.

Actually, of all the rays, only the stingray is dangerous to man, and sharks are limited in the damage they can do because of their inability to stop short or back up.

Bony Fishes. One order of modern bony fishes, that to which the sturgeon belongs, is quite archaic. At one time, fish like these dominated in the seas. Sturgeons have small mouths and weak jaws that can be swung downward and forward when they feed. The upper lobe of the tail is somewhat longer than the lower. Although their ancestors had bony skeletons, sturgeons are more cartilaginous than other bony fish and have fewer scales.

The sturgeonlike fish were succeeded by fish much more like the modern garpike. These fish have shorter, deeper bodies and a tail that is almost symmetrical. There is an armor of thick scales and a long, crocodilelike snout.

Both these early groups were replaced by fish that went further in shortening the tail and making it symmetrical. The scales were thinned down more and there were advances in the structure of the skull, particularly the jaw mechanism. This line of fish evolution gave rise to most of the modern bony fishes.

Salmon, herrings, and trout are some of the most primitive members of this conquering group. They are fish with soft rays in their fins, an open duct to the air bladder, and pelvic fins that are placed far back on the body.

Carp and goldfish are somewhat more advanced. Their specialization consists of having the front vertebrae form a chain of bones that connects the air bladder to the inner ear.

Eels broke away early from this main line of evolution. They have no pelvic fins and the back and belly fins are usually combined with the tail fin. Most of them lack scales.

Pike and sticklefish are intermediate between the carp and the most advanced fishes. There is an advance in the structure of the shoulder girdle, and the air bladder has an opening that is continuous with the gut. The fins have soft rays.

The most highly developed fishes have stiff rays at the front of the back and belly fins. The duct of the air bladder is closed, the body shortened, and the pelvic fins are situated far forward. The peak of this evolutionary triumph can be observed in the modern perch.

While most of the bony fishes were evolving in the manner described above, one line remained quite distinct. This line had no rays in the fins, but fleshy lobes instead. The coelacanth, from deep in the oceans around southeastern Africa, is a living reminder of ancient days. Although not very successful as fishes, the lobe-fins are very important to vertebrate history, for it was a lobe-fin that took the first daring step from sea to land and ultimately became the first amphibian.

With a mouthful of teeth worthy of a wolf, the moray eel on the opposite page lunges from his hiding place in the reef. Morays are powerful marine predators, that constitute their own family within the eel group.

Flounders and soles have the ability to change their color to match the bottom surface on which they rest. The young of these highly specialized fish are "normal" in appearance. As they grow older, they settle on the bottom on one side. The eye on the underside then moves across to the top surface to join the other eye already there.

Coral fishes such as this butterfly fish (bottom right) frequently sport very brilliant colors. This appears to be a device for "signalling" territory limits to others of their species.

This bottom-dwelling weaverfish (below, left) has poison spines along the back and on the cheek region. These fishes stay near the bottom and frequently bury themselves under the sand.

Amphibians

Amphibians were the first vertebrates to adapt to the land, and for a short while they had it all to themselves. Of course, there were invertebrates, such as spiders, but these satisfied hunger and offered no competition. During those days, the amphibians developed in many different ways, and a great variety of forms appeared. One of the oldest lines of amphibians are known as labyrinthodonts and it is among this group that the characteristics typical of amphibians were developed. Some of these early types clung pretty much to the water, but others developed into active land-dwellers, sometimes reaching a length of six feet. Some were heavily armored, some had strange body proportions with huge, flat heads and tiny feet. Another type, the lepospondyls, never became very large and lived mostly in swampy areas. Some of them were legless with snakelike bodies. Others had wide, triangular heads.

From all these early amphibians, each developing in its own way, there evolved only three orders that are still in existence today. Those of labyrinthodont descent are the anurans, or salientians, better known as frogs and toads, and a very successful group. Today there are some frog species in every continent except Antarctica. Toads are absent in Australia and the Antarctic. Toads are not as quick as frogs, but have an additional protection to make up for their lack of speed. This is a bitter substance exuded from skin glands, which discourages any predator from taking a toad into its mouth. Frogs and toads are not equipped to live in deserts, of course, although they are remarkably adept at finding moisture in semi-arid situations. Nor do they live near

The Old World newt shown below is terrestrial for most of the year, but becomes aquatic during the breeding season. The male then appears very beautiful with a frilled red crest on his back contrasting with his spotted body.

the sea, as salt water is fatal to these amphibians. They are able to withstand extremes in temperature, and so there are frogs and toads in the Yukon as well as in the equatorial forests.

There are 2600 species of anurans, which in spite of their differences, still have common characteristics that clearly separate them from the other amphibians. They are the only tailless members of the class and their long hind legs are quite distinct. Frogs and toads have no neck and as a consequence cannot turn their heads easily. Anurans use their hind legs in swimming, while salamanders rely on the tail for propulsion.

Although many individual salamanders may be seen in a favorable environment at a given moment, there are far fewer species of this order than in the anurans. Salamanders and newts, known as the caudates, number just 225 species, which, like the toads and frogs,

live in moist areas throughout the world. There are, however, no caudates in South America or Australia, nor are they to be found in most parts of Africa.

Many species of salamanders spend their adult lives on land in moist underbrush, while a few actually live in trees. Others live an aquatic existence and some of these, found in deep, cold waters, never make the transformation from larva to adult. They do reach sexual maturity, enabling them to breed, while still retaining their gills and other larval characteristics. Other salamanders spend their lives in moist caves and in these places of eternal darkness have found sight an unnecessary sense and are blind.

Each caudate species has its own courtship pattern. The female of one species will not respond to the ritual advances of a male of any other species, thus keeping each group distinct.

The California slender salamander pictured at left below has tiny legs unsuited to walking, and moves sinuously like a snake. Although it likes to live in burrows, this salamander is incapable of digging one and has to "borrow" those of other animals. Otherwise it rests under logs with its body tightly coiled like a snake's.

The fire salamanders mate on land in July, and it is not until the following May that the female enters the water to give birth to live young. There can be anywhere from 10 to 50 one-inch-long young in a litter, and each has well-developed arms and legs. Gills are still present, however, so some metamorphosis is necessary. When adult, these fire salamander larvae (bottom left) will be completely terrestrial.

Central American caecelians, like the one at the lower right, are burrowing amphibians without limbs. Their eyes are small and weak, but a tentacle between the eye and nose acts as a sense organ in the subterranean world caecilians inhabit.

The general shape of the salamander's body, coupled with the shortness of the legs and the length of the tail, makes locomotion different from that seen in the anurans. They are creepers rather than jumpers, although when alarmed, many species do leap. When relaxed, caudates like to stroll along the bottoms of the ponds they frequent.

The wormlike caecilians are mysterious amphibians. Living in burrows beneath the ground, the caecilian's pattern of life is a private affair, almost unknown to man. Although at a casual gance the caecilians look like earthworms, they can easily be distinguished by the presence of a mouth and eyes. Actually, the eyes are useless, for they are quite blind and "see" by means of a small touch-sensitive tentacle that lies between the eye and the mouth. They have no legs and, as one might suspect in a burrowing animal, the head is blunt and the tail short.

Caecilians belong to the third order of amphibians, the Gymnophiona, of which there are 75 species, most of which live in Central and South America. Others can be found in the warm parts of Africa and Asia.

The eastern spadefoot toad, shown at the right, lives in sandy lowlands of the eastern United States. There is a crescent-shaped horny projection on the inner border of each hind foot, which forms a permanent shovel for digging out burrows. During mating time, the males sing in chorus with a penetrating sound something like the cawing of a crow. Egg masses of 1,000 to 2,500 are deposited in bands wrapped around water plants.

The golden mantella of Madagascar (opposite page, top) is quite different from the other "true" frogs of its family, the Ranidae, for it has short legs and a small, broad body. But other anatomical similarities definitely place it in this group.

The European natterjack toad (opposite page, bottom) is distinguished by its very short legs, which make it impossible for this toad to hop. Instead, natterjacks are able to run almost as quickly as a mouse. When threatened, the natterjack assumes a butting position and inflates its body.

The skin of a caecilian is different from that of other amphibians, for though it feels slimy on the outside, beneath the surface there are small scales.

Caecilians can grow to be as long as four feet, but they are never very wide. The largest diameter known is only one inch. Some females do give live birth and these, of course, become quite stout temporarily. Caecilians probably live on a diet of earthworms and termites, although no one is really sure, and they are themselves considered delectable by several species of snakes.

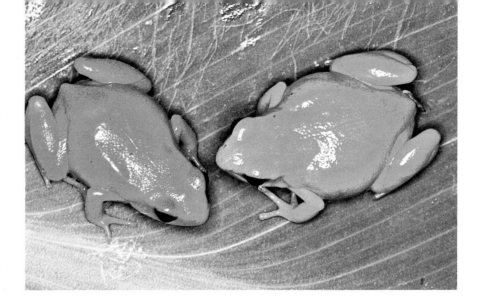

Reptiles

Some of the labyrinthodont amphibians became frogs and toads, but others took a very different evolutionary route—one which led to the reptiles. The big innovation of these early reptiles was the development of the amniote egg. This egg, which is fertilized inside the female's body by the male, is sometimes laid in a depression in the ground or less frequently carried within the mother until hatching time. In either case, it serves the purpose of freeing the animal completely of the necessity to return to the water to breed. Thus, the reptiles were able to take over more of the surface of the land and exploit many more of the situations unavailable to the moisture-clinging amphibians. The amniote egg is comprised of a sac holding the embryo suspended in a pool of liquid, another sac that contains the waste products given off by the embryo and a huge quantity of yolk from which the embryo feeds. It is all surrounded by a thick, leathery shell that adequately protects from the elements, while pores allow oxygen to pass in and carbon dioxide out.

Once this egg had evolved, the reptiles branched out greatly, and eventually took over as the ruling animals of the world. There were medium to enormous reptiles on land—those we call dinosaurs. Some went further and took to the skies on leathery wings. Others, oddly enough, after having won the battle for land supremacy, reverted to a watery environment.

For millions of years, the reptiles held sway. Their success was overwhelming. Then environmental conditions changed, and, one by one, the impressive ruling reptiles died out, leaving just those small to medium-sized reptiles we know today.

The 250-million-year-old fossil below is that of Seymouria, clearly a four-footed vertebrate, yet a constant source of argument to zoologists. It is one of the linking forms between amphibians and reptiles and for that reason hard to assign to either class. Many of the features of the skeleton are like those of the labyrinthodont amphibians, yet there are others, particularly in the skull and the hip region, that spell "reptile". In any case, Seymouria with its large head, stocky body and sprawled-out limbs gives an idea of what the earliest reptiles looked like.

(opposite) Turtles are regarded as highly specialized, yet basically very primitive reptiles. The specialization lies in the anatomy of their body armor and in their horny, beaked jaws. In other features, however, such as their skull and limbs, they are very much like the stem reptiles called cotylosaurs.

The four living orders are: The Chelonia (turtles), the Crocodilia (crocodiles), the Rhynchocephalia (tuataras), and the Squamata (lizards and snakes). The tuataras live only in New Zealand and probably have been fairly restricted throughout their history. The crocodilians have done very well in the tropical areas of the world, while the snakes, lizards, and turtles have thrived in many varied locations. Although no longer dominant, the reptiles of today are a very successful class.

The first turtles made their appearance during the Age of Dinosaurs and have remained relatively unchanged since that time. The heavy shell that characterizes this order was already present in those ancient days, but turtles may not have been able to pull in their heads and legs for the complete protection most of them now enjoy.

There are about 400 species of turtles, which are sometimes called tortoises and occasionally terrapins. Some varieties live out most of their lives on land, while others are more aquatic, preferring the calm of a small pond. There are species that inhabit the seas of the world and those that live in burrows in the desert sands.

In general, turtles that live on land have sturdy columnar legs to support the bulk of the shell in moving across hard ground. Marine turtles have less shell for extra buoyancy and generally grow to be larger than the land species. The legs of sea turtles are flipperlike to aid in swimming while pond turtles have webbed feet. Turtles range in size from about 12 inches to almost 6 feet, the largest of them weighing upward of 1,000 pounds. They live in all the temperate regions of the world, including Australia.

Land turtles live on a varied diet with the emphasis on vegetation. Water turtles are more carnivorous, feeding on fish, worms, and other vertebrates.

Crocodilians inhabit only the tropics and subtropics. The large, aggressive crocodilians are the closest surviving relatives of the dinosaurs, and in many respects they are the most advanced of reptiles. They have, for instance, a heart that is four-chambered, socketed teeth, and a palate that separates the mouth from the

The Nile crocodile below is a typical crocodilian, a group which also includes the alligators and the long-snouted gavials. Crocodilians are the only surviving archosaurs (or ruling reptiles), the others being the extinct dinosaurs and gliding reptiles. Zoologists frequently turn to the crocodile when they try to imagine what the soft parts and behavior of dinosaurs were like.

nasal canals. The first known crocodile was rather small, with its hind legs larger than the forelimbs, indicating its descent from a two-legged ancestor. Other types appeared, some of which became marine animals with paddlelike legs, and a tail-fin.

Today's crocodilians of the order Crocodilia or Loricata number about 25 species, divided into three families: the gavials, the alligators, and the crocodiles. They all look quite similar, but can be distinguished by their snouts: that of the gavial is long and slender; the alligator's is blunt and short; and the crocodile's lies somewhere in-between.

All crocodilians have a protective covering of bony plates inside the skin across the back, but as these plates are not fused, the crocodilians are capable of great flexibility and speed. They have webbed feet, and the eyes, nostrils, and ears are placed high on the head, allowing these reptiles to be almost completely submerged without loss of their senses. They have large, strong jaws, and very sharp teeth, enabling them to hunt and eat fish and meat with efficiency.

The tuatara from New Zealand (top) is the only living species of a whole order of reptiles, the rhynchocephalians. This lone survivor is grouped with the lizards and snakes rather than the archosaurian crocodiles. In its youth, the tuatara has a transluscent scale covering a third eye on top of the head. This is not really too unusual as many extinct lower vertebrates had an opening in the skull for such a median eye, and several living lizards still possess this structure. These "third" eyes do not form clear visual images, but seem to regulate exposure to light and heat.

The four-foot-long skull (center) of the largest flesh-eating dinosaur, Tyrannosaurus rex, has six-inch teeth, each of which is serrated along the edges for better slicing action.

This three-foot-long East Indian water lizard lives among the forests and streams. The function of the sailfin tail seems to be to propel it by sculling from side to side while swimming. Bony outgrowths from the tail vertebrae support the "sailfin".

Lizards and snakes belong to the order Squamata and form the largest and most diverse group of living reptiles. There are almost 6,000 species. The Squamates have enjoyed this great diversity almost since the end of the Age of Dinosaurs. Early species were quite lizardlike and, indeed, many modern lizards retain primitive characteristics such as unsocketed teeth. The snakes are the youngest of all the reptiles, although their line goes back millions of years. Their adaptations in the form of leglessness, elongation of the body, and widely opening jaws have stood them in good stead since their beginnings. Because snakes are low to the ground, they can hide easily in debris or under rocks. The additional

advantage possessed by those species which are poisonous is obvious.

Lizards range in size from a few inches to ten feet in length. There are running, climbing, gliding, and burrowing forms. Some lizards are legless like snakes, but they have movable eyelids and their lower jaws are different.

Lizards inhabit most of the warm and temperate areas of the world, including the deserts, which are enjoyed by several species.

Snakes are probably descended from burrowing lizards. Unlike lizards, snakes do not possess movable eyelids; they have eyelids that are fused together, giving them an odd, fixed stare But the main difference is in the lack of fusion between the two parts of the lower jaw

The cobra's dire reputation (left) is well founded. Its nerve poison is quite deadly and injected with great efficiency by way of four fangs, two on each side of the upper jaw. The cobra assumes a defensive and warning posture when it feels threatened, with a third of its body raised above the flat coil on the ground, the hood widely expanded, and the head directed forward. The hood is spread by means of elongate ribs that can be erected to force out the loose skin behind the head.

Probably the most dangerous of all venomous snakes because of the extreme potency of its poison is the saw-scaled viper pictured at left. It inhabits deserts and semideserts from North Africa to India. When annoyed, it puffs out its body, throws it into a figure eight and rubs the sides of its coils against one another. The rasping rough scales produce a hissing sound like violently boiling water.

which permits widening so that the snake can swallow objects larger than its own diameter.

Snakes live on the ground, in trees, in burrows, and in the water. There are even marine snakes in the oceans of the world.

Most snakes live in the tropics, but there are species in the colder parts of the world. Indeed, one type has even been found within the Arctic Circle. Areas with no snakes at all are Iceland, Ireland, and New Zealand.

The tuatara is the only surviving member of the ancient order Rhynchocephalia. The single species is found only on a few islands off New Zealand. At first glance tuataras look like large lizards, but their skull is differently constructed and more primitive.

Turkeys are strictly New World birds associated in particular with the United States by virtue of their annual presence at the Thanksgiving dinner table. This ocellated turkey (upper left) is, however, more southerly in distribution, being found in Yucatan, Guatemala, and British Honduras. It lives in bushy lowlands that are partially forested. The word "turkey" refers to the "turk, turk" sound made by the bird and has nothing to do with the country, Turkey, where it has never been found in nature.

The kiwi (upper right) is a peculiar bird of New Zealand. It is a relative of the extinct giant moas. Kiwis have nostril openings near the tip of the bill and possess a fine sense of smell, unlike other birds, which depend more on sight. There are no external wings and no tail feathers. The eggs are over five inches long and weigh more than a pound. Kiwis live in dense forests in burrows, where they sleep by day and from which they emerge at night to hunt.

Egrets (right) belong to the heron family and are typified by slim bodies, long, slender bills and exquisite ornamental plumage. Most egrets are gregarious, and feed and nest together in large groups.

Birds

During the days of the dinosaurs, some of the ruling reptiles began to adapt to flight. Some of them retained all their reptilian characteristics and added membranes of skin attached to one long finger and the sides of the body to serve as wings. Others went on to develop feathers and ultimately other birdlike characteristics. The first of these, the pterosaurs, became extinct along with the dinosaurs. The latter, the birds, have been remarkably successful since their advent.

Archaeopteryx was one of the first birds. It had a reptilian skull, a long neck and a long bony tail. But there were feathers, and the jaws which probably housed teeth were, nevertheless, beak-shaped. Also, *Archaeopteryx* had a large brain case, indicating the sort of complex nervous system necessary to a flying vertebrate.

In time, the birds became less reptilian and typical bird characteristics appeared. The bones of the hand were fused, the pelvis became firmly anchored to the back, and the bony tail was reduced. The breastbone became enlarged for the attachment of wing muscles.

Modern birds are enormously varied, there being almost 9,000 living species, divided into 28 orders. They are all quite similar to one another in basic structure, but differ in proportions and living habits. All birds have feathers and wings, even those that do not fly. No modern bird has teeth; the sharp beak serves for cutting or crushing in their stead. There are birds in every area of the world; even the frigid Antarctic can boast of penguins. In fact, because of their fantastic migrations, the same species can be seen in Canada at one season and in South America at another.

Generally speaking, those birds that cannot fly are larger and have much stronger legs than those that do. In the running birds, like ostriches, rheas, and cassowaries, the wings are very much reduced in size. Their bones are heavier, having no air cavities as do those of flying birds. Although they do not fly, ostriches and rheas are fast runners, with feet that are long and strong.

Penguins, too, are flightless birds, but rather than running speed, they depend upon swimming ability. Underwater, they are able to swim as fast as seals.

Kiwis, too, are flightless, but they differ from other flightless birds in several respects. They have nostrils near the tip of the bill, providing them with a well-developed sense of smell, something very rare for birds, who, like man, rely much more heavily on their sight. There is no external trace of a wing, nor are there tail feathers of any kind. Actually, the entire body is covered with feathers which look more like hair. Kiwis live in the dense forest and if they are in a hurry can outrun a dog, although they have an awkward waddle when walking.

In contrast to the flightless birds, the albatrosses of the cold southerly reaches of the globe, are almost unbelievable masters of the skies. Some albatrosses make a complete round-the-world tour between breeding seasons. The wandering albatross has the largest wing span of any living bird, measuring almost 12 feet.

Second to flight, the ability most admired in birds is song. The range of sounds used for communication in these winged vertebrates is exceptional, but some of our best-loved birds are mute. This is true of the stork, who compensates by way of an elaborate series of postures and a wild clacking of the beak.

Some swans are also mute, but, in general, most of the birds of the family Anatidae, which includes ducks, geese, and swans, have loud, raucous voices. All the waterfowl have short legs and a short, broad bill. Most of them are excellent fliers, in addition to being great swimmers.

The birds of prey, which are all marvelous fliers, are divided into two orders. Those that fly by day, the eagles, hawks, and vultures, belong to the order Falconiformes. They are all beautifully adapted predators, with long wings for sustained flight and feet ending in sharp talons, for tearing apart flesh. Their eyesight is keener than that of most vertebrates, for there are two focusing points in each eye, one for close objects and another for those in the distance. The powerful beak is sharply hooked. The entire body, even in the smallest hawks, gives the impression of great power.

The night-hunters are, of course, the owls belonging to the order Strigiformes. They are different from the Falconiformes in their very soft, downy feathers which reach to the toes, and the out-sized head with its small beak and huge, frontally set eyes. Although owls can make some terrifying sounds when at leisure, while they are at work hunting they are absolutely silent, an ability enhanced by their soft plumage.

During breeding time, boobies (opposite page) like to flock together in groups on the oceanic islands near the schools of fish they prey upon. From these rocks, they may dive as far as 100 feet down to the sea.

The hornbill (left) has mating habits as peculiar as its appearance. After mating, the female enters a cavity in a tree and fashions a barrier of mud, earth, and droppings across the opening. She leaves a slit just large enough for her bill and thus protects the young from predators, striking out with sharp thrusts through the slit.

The toucan's bill (below) is also enormous, but as it is filled with air, it is surprisingly light and forms no obstacle to flight. It is a fine tool for tearing off fruits and berries.

The peacock (center) is really just a fancy chicken, belonging to the order from which the best game birds, like the Canada geese below, as well as the domestic fowl are derived.

The European spoonbill (right) is closely related to the ibises and like them is very gregarious. Both fly with the neck extended, but spoonbills form a wide V formation and do not indulge in group gliding. This spoonbill breeds in marshes in nests about one foot above the mud. The large bill is used like a scythe, sweeping over the water to filter out the small invertebrates this bird feeds upon.

The California quail (bottom) lives in grasslands and semiarid areas and is able to go for months without drinking water. Although quail can fly, they spend much of their time on the ground and frequently run rather than fly when alarmed.

Of all the birds, those of the order Galliformes have been most important to mankind. It is from among these birds that we derive our domestic fowl as well as our favorite game birds. Chickens, turkeys, pheasants, partridges, grouse, and quail all belong in this order. Characteristic of every one is a small head on a thick-set body. The legs are long, and the strong feet are built for scratching the earth in search of seeds. Most species have short wings, precluding the possibility of long migratory flights. Most of these species boast males of exquisite plumage, high combs, wattles, and spurs. A striking example of a gallinaceous male can be seen in the peacock.

The constant drumming sounds made by

woodpeckers of the order Piciformes, as they drill their way through to food, is enough to bring them to anyone's attention. Once noticed, they continue to captivate with their straight-tailed vertical hopping up and down insect-laden trees.

Over half the species of living birds belong to a single order—the Passeriformes. These include all our songbirds, such as the robins, wrens, sparrows, and cardinals. In addition to the beauty added to our lives by the lilting song of these small birds, there is an economic reason for their popularity. For songbirds are indispensable agents in ridding the world of agricultural pests such as locusts and caterpillars.

Passerines occur in all the major land areas of the world except Antarctica and dominate the world of the air. Their hallmark is the foot, which has four toes joined at the same level, three in front and one behind, of which the hind toe is the strongest. The purpose of such a foot is to grasp firmly to a small perch while offering full support to the bird. This foot is also useful in hopping or walking. We are more likely, however, to be aware of the highly developed voice box, which is their other outstanding feature.

The scarlet macaw (left) is a member of the parrot family. Parrots fly straight and very rapidly.

Eagles, like the magnificent golden eagle (below) use all forms of flight in their hunting. They are particularly expert at soaring.

The booby (left) flies with head, neck and body in a straight line, with the wings extended out to the sides, looking like an airplane.

Mammals

Long ago, in the very beginning of reptile evolution, before the advent of dinosaurs, one line of reptiles took a completely different path from the others, developing into animals with teeth designed for cutting and chewing rather than grabbing and swallowing whole. The vertebral column was very strong, and the legs, which lifted the body high off the ground, had knees pointing forward and elbows pointing backward. These reptiles were, in fact, almost mammalian and are referred to as mammal-like reptiles. From the mammal-like reptiles, it was a short step to the complete mammal—an animal distinguished by its con-

Looking at this group of lions, no one can doubt that the mammals have taken over as rulers of the land. This title, once held by the amphibians and later by the reptiles, was inherited by the mammals 70 million years ago, after the fall of the dinosaurs. There are now 28 orders of living mammals in the world, of which the Carnivora form one. Mammals of this order are hunters of meat, and the great cats are at the peak of evolutionary perfection as predators par excellence.

stant high body temperature, its external covering of hair and fur, and its production of milk for the young.

The first mammals were rather innocuous animals: small, scurrying creatures that existed on insects. Inasmuch as they were inhabiting what was then the dinosaur's world, it was probably just as well that they were inconspicuous. For millions of years, while the reptiles triumphed, the mammals remained modest forest creatures. Then, when the dinosaurs became extinct, the mammals, seizing their opportunity, began to expand in both numbers and varieties. Quite suddenly, the world became a mammal-dominated place and has remained so to this day.

Lions live harmoniously in groups called prides, consisting of individuals of both sexes and all ages. Once the plains-loving lions roamed freely from Africa through to India, but they have been greatly restricted by mankind and now live only in protected areas of Africa and the Gir forest in India. In hunting, usually of large, hoofed animals, the females do most of the actual work, while the male serves primarily as an intimidating decoy. A large lion can attain eight feet in length and weigh over 500 pounds.

The mammals are a highly diversified class. Here are six representatives of different mammal groups: (top, left) an Old World mouse of the order Rodentia; (bottom, left) an Australian wombat of the Marsupialia; (top, right) a three-toed sloth of the Edentata; (opposite page, left) an orangutan of the Primates; (opposite page, upper right) a rabbit of the Lagomorpha and (opposite page, below) an aardvark of the order Tubulidentata.

From almost the earliest part of mammalian history, there have been two distinct groups: the marsupial mammals and the placental mammals. Most living mammals belong to the placental group. The name denotes the presence of the internal structure known as a placenta, by way of which the young are nourished while within the mother's body. Marsupials have, instead, a pouch into which their barely formed young crawl after birth for future development at the mother's nipple.

Marsupials have been less successful than placental mammals in that there are fewer of them and they are now restricted in range to Australia and parts of North and South America. In addition to their less advanced method of reproduction, marsupials have the disadvantage of an inferior intelligence.

In North and South America, there are few living marsupials, although at one time in their history, they were more diverse. The most flourishing marsupial has been the opossum which has spread out in recent years to increase its range northward.

Australia, which has remained remote throughout most of history, has been the real haven of the marsupials, which, until the coming of man, had the whole continent to themselves with no placental competition (except for a few adventurous rats). Here we find an extraordinary range of animals—plains-dwelling grazers like the kangaroos, shy arboreal creatures such as koalas, and fierce predators like Tasmanian "wolves" and "devils."

A third more primitvie group of mammals also exists in Australia and New Zealand. This group, called the monotremes, are egg-laying mammals that relate more closely to their rep-

tile ancestors than either the marsupials or placentals. The skeleton in several respects is quite similar to that of the reptiles. Although monotremes are warm-blooded, their temperatures fluctuate more than those of other mammals. The platypus and the echidna form the two families within this order.

The other 16 orders of mammals all belong in the placental category. These animals, beginning with small insectivore forebears, have spread out and diversified in so many shapes and sizes that their dominance is obvious. Adaptations of every sort have been made, so that there are mammals that fly, and mammals that swim, mammals that climb trees and mammals that dig burrows, as well as those that live on land. There are plant-eaters, meat-eaters, insect-eaters, and carrion-eaters. Big and small, the mammals are the rulers.

The most ancient order of placental mammals and in many ways the most primitive, is that of the Insectivora. Insectivores are small and inconspicuous and include such animals as shrews, moles, and hedgehogs. Most of them have long snouts, small, sharp teeth and five clawed toes on each foot.

Bats and flying lemurs, because of their special aerial adaptations, are placed in separate orders—the Chiroptera and the Dermoptera, respectively. They are, however, quite similar to the insectivores in all aspects other than their flying abilities. Bats are second only to the rodents in number of species—there are about 750, which have varied habits and diets. Flying lemurs are not lemurs, nor do they actually fly. They are built for gliding, and the common name colugo is probably less confusing.

Sloths, anteaters, and armadillos are all members of the order Edentata (meaning without teeth). Sloths and armadillos do have some teeth although these lack enamel. There are 30 species in this order, all of which live in South America, Central America, or the southern part of North America.

At one time, rabbits and hares and pikas were classified as rodents, but they are separated now into a new order—the Lagomorpha. They occupied a great portion of the land areas of the world before the coming of man, and since then have been introduced, with overwhelming success, into those regions they had overlooked.

Pangolins are unique kinds of animal and the eight species constitute their own order, the Pholidota. They live only in the tropics of Africa and Asia, and their body is covered with overlapping sharp-edged scales, which are movable.

The rodents, of course, are the most flourishing of all mammals in terms of numbers and adaptability. There are 3,000 different species belonging to the Rodentia; included among them are rats, mice, squirrels, gophers, guinea pigs, hamsters, gerbils, porcupines,

Rhinoceroses are members of a declining order —the perissodactyls, of which horses and tapirs are other important members. Once, this was a highly diverse group inhabiting much of the earth's surface. Now the only wild horses are in Mongolia; the zebras and wild asses are steadily declining, while tapirs can be found only in South America and parts of Asia. The five species of rhinoceros inhabit parts of Asia and Africa, but are rapidly dying out. The rhinos pictured here are African black rhinoceroses and live in eastern and southern Africa. This is the most common species, but the aphrodisiac qualities attributed to its horn are contributing to the constant decimation of its numbers, as it is hunted assiduously by natives for sale in China. Black rhinos have a prehensile tip on the upper lip, which helps in browsing on leaves and twigs. They are short-tempered and unpredictable and have been known to throw men into the air with the front horn.

The antelopes (left) belong to an order of hoofed mammals, the Artiodactyla, which have been far more successful than the perissodactyls. Mankind's most important meat animals belong to this group —pigs, sheep, goats and cattle, for instance, in addition to game animals like deer and also favorite zoo animals such as giraffes.

The gorilla (below) is the rarest as well as the largest of manlike apes of the order Primates. Average height for one of these massive creatures is about five feet with the knees bent, and the chest measures about 70 inches in circumference.

beavers, and muskrats, to name but a few. All have four constantly growing incisors, two above and two below, with a space between them and the cheek teeth.

The Cetacea is the order including the largest animals of all times, the whales. All told, there are 90 species of whales and porpoises living in the oceans of the world. Cetaceans have adapted completely to the sea and never return to the land from which their ancestors came.

This black panther is really a member of the leopard family. Note the size of the teeth which are used to kill its prey.

137

Carnivora is the name of the order to which the great hunters among the mammals belong. Wolves, lions, weasels, mongooses, and hyenas are all carnivores, as are domestic dogs and cats. But non-hunting animals such as the pandas are also members of this group, as are the omnivorous bears and racoons. Most carnivores are running or climbing animals, but the otters are aquatic. All species have clawed feet, well-developed brains and one pair of cheek teeth specially developed for shearing, called carnassials.

Closely related to the Carnivora are the members of the Pinnipedia—seals, sea lions, and walruses. There are 31 species along the coasts of the world, the majority of which live in temperate or polar waters. They have torpedo-shaped bodies with all four legs transformed into flippers.

The peculiar aardvarks arep laced in a separate order—the Tubulidentata. They live in Southern Africa, anywhere large colonies of ants and termites are to be found.

Two species of elephants are the only remaining members of the Proboscidea, although not too long ago there were many more kinds of these massive animals roaming throughout every continent except Australia. Aside from their great size, the elephant's most conspicuous characteristic is the trunk, a long, flexible extension of the nose.

Oddly enough, the two orders most closely related to the Proboscidea are the Hyracoidea and the Sirenia. The first of these includes the

little hyraxes, or conies, of biblical fame. Hyraxes look like rodents, but they have flat, hooflike nails rather than claws.

The Sirenia are the dugongs and manatees sometimes referred to as sea cows. They live along tropical coasts, grazing on water vegetation. They have fore legs that are paddle-shaped, but no hind legs.

Perissodactyls are hoofed plant-eaters with an odd number of toes. At one time, there were many families, but now there are only three—horses, tapirs, and rhinoceroses. They are all well-adapted to running, their common characteristic being that the weight-bearing axis of the foot passes through the middle toe. That toe, then, is either the biggest or the sole remaining one in the foot.

Even-toed plant-eaters, classified as the Artiodactyla, have been much more successful. There are nine living families, which include several of our most important food animals. Pigs, hippopotamuses, camels, deer, giraffes, antelopes, sheep, goats, and cattle all belong in this order. Artiodactyls bear their weight between the third and fourth toe. They always retain at least these two toes, making most of them cloven-hoofed.

Primates are of great interest to mankind, for it is the order to which we belong. There are several families in the order: lemurs, tarsiers, monkeys, and apes are some of them. Most primates live in tropical areas. Common to the order are forwardly directed eyes, grasping hands, and a well-developed brain.

Mammals have adapted to every sort of environment. The hippo at left, is a swamp-dwelling animal of tropical Africa that spends much of its time lolling in the mud. The tapir (right) lives in wooded areas of Mexico and Central and South America. Dolphins (bottom) are completely aquatic mammals found in all the oceans of the world.

139

This is a colony of small, saclike animals called sea squirts, or tunicates. They are chordates, along with the fish-shaped lancelet (bottom, opposite page) and all the vertebrates. These primitive attached forms consist mainly of their feeding apparatus— a slitted basketlike structure through which water is moved, while the food particles are extracted and remain inside the animal.

"Missing Links" Between Vertebrates and Invertebrates

Animals with backbones made up of separate discs called vertebrae are all fairly obviously related. It does not strain the imagination to conceive of fishes, amphibians, reptiles, and mammals as sharing many common denominators of ancestry and relationship. But what of the first vertebrates, the agnathans, or jaw-less fishes, of which the living lampreys and hagfishes are now the sole survivors? How do they tie in with about twenty different major kinds of invertebrates?

Actually, the vertebrates can be put together with several relatively insignificant kinds of marine animals into a common major grouping or phylum called the chordates. The common character uniting all these organisms is the possession of an internal stiffening rod called a notochord, present in all vertebrates during their embryonic development and usually replaced later by bony or cartilaginous discs. In the other chordates, the notochord remains an unsegmented rod, or disappears entirely in the adult.

A very representative kind of chordate and one that furnishes an almost ideal transitional kind of morphology between an invertebrate chordate and the vertebrates is the lancelet amphioxus, technically called *Branchiostoma*. Amphioxus is only about two inches long and lives all around the world in shallow, sandy-bottomed off-shore situations. It is basically fishlike in shape with structures that can be seen to lead quite naturally into those of jawless fishes. The head region is not set off from the rest of the body and has no separate eyes, nose, ears, or jaws. The front third of the animal, however, behind the mouth, is provided with several hundred gill slits, piercing the pharynx and covered by folds of the body wall. Feeding as well as respiration takes place by way of currents set up by thousands of tiny hairs on the cells that line the gill bars between the slits. Water containing food particles (and also oxygen) is drawn in through the mouth into the pharynx and expelled through the slits. The food particles get stuck to a slimy mucus that is secreted by a tract of ciliated cells along the bottom and which move the entrapped food further down the gut.

Although there are many differences between a true vertebrates such as a jawless fish and the invertebrate chordate amphioxus, the similarities are overwhelming. In addition to skeletal gill bars, there is, of course, the all important internal stiffening rod the notochord. Above the latter lies a hollow central nerve cord, and below it the digestive tube. The body musculature, too, is segmented into the familiar fishlike muscle blocks or myotomes. All in all, although no good fossil evidence exists, we can conclude that the first vertebrates must have passed through an amphioxuslike stage.

There is another group of invertebrate chordates that, unlike amphioxus, seem very far-fetched indeed as relatives to fish and man. These are the sea squirts, or tunicates. The majority of these animals are small, saclike creatures attached to the sea floor and obtaining their food by filter-feeding. The body is mainly a huge pharynx slitted with openings that are lined with ciliated cells. Right here we can see the similarity to the feeding apparatus described for amphioxus. However, to find more apparent chordate characters, we

The photograph on the bottom shows clearly the segmented musculature of amphioxus. The structure of the pharynx, with its hundreds of gill openings, can be seen from the diagrammatic section above the photograph. As water is circulated through the gill-basket, a mucus-coated groove, the endostyle, carries food particles farther back into the gut. Observe the notochord and overlying nerve cord along the back. This kind of arrangement is also typical for the vertebrates.

The free-moving larvae of certain tunicates look like tadpoles (far left). The head region contains sense organs and a feeding device called an endostyle and similar to that found in amphioxus.

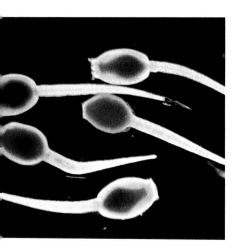

have to turn to the larval tunicate. These larvae, unlike their parents, are not attached but free-swimming. They have a tadpolelike appearance with a head, and a tail region through which runs the by now familiar notochord, below a hollow central nerve canal. An interesting, even if unproven, theory is that some hundreds of millions of years ago, certain ancient tunicate larvae, instead of developing into sessile adults, by-passed this stage by a process which can be observed among species of animals today. This is the process of "paedomorphosis" which consists of the development of sexual maturity during a larval morphological stage, so that the adults now actually look like the larvae of their ancestors. "Precocious" tunicate larvae, then, became the ancestors of the amphioxuslike forms which were at the base of all the vertebrates.

Thus far, we have speculated about relationships among the chordate invertebrates, but what about thenonchordate invertebrates; that is, the worms, the snails, the crabs, and the star fish? Where among these many varied body plans should we look for chordate relatives? Oddly enough, it turns out that the group to which the starfish, sea urchins, sea cucumbers and sea lilies belong, the echino-

derms, are the closest living invertebrate relatives to the chordates. Among the many kinds of invertebrates, only the echinoderms have essential characters in common with the chordates in the manner in which the fertilized eggs first develop. There are also features of the nervous system, the development of muscle fibers and hard parts, and certain very specific biochemical similarities which all point toward echinoderms, rather than for instance, earthworms or crabs, as the closest invertebrate link to primitive chordates and vertebrates. The larvae of echinoderms, too, provide a clue to possible relationships. Echinoderm larvae, unlike the radially symmetrical adults, are bilaterally symmetrical; that is, only as in tunicate larvae, amphioxus, and vertebrates, do the two halves of the body form mirror images. Some zoologists have hypothesized that ancient sessile echinoderms and chordates shared a common and as yet completely unknown ancestor whose echinodermlike larvae became transformed into the kind of larvae now possessed by tunicates. Then through "paedomorphosis," what was then the typically adult chordate character of being an attached filter-feeder was by-passed. Instead, selective emphasis was placed on the larval characteristics of free motion through the water. The fish shape and the segmented musculature around the incompressible notochord were a result of this selection. Ciliary filter-feeding by way of the slitted pharynx remained in vogue through the amphioxus stage and did not change basically until certain fishes developed movable jaws. Respiration which had been a by-product of the pharyngeal filter-feeding, then became the main function of the gill system.

The main evolutionary steps then between invertebrates and vertebrates would be the following: An attached echinodermlike ancestor gives rise to a kind of tunicate whose larvae reproduce while still in the free-swimming stage. These in turn pass through an amphioxuslike evolutionary stage before giving rise to the first vertebrates, the jawless fishes.

Shown below is the larva of a starfish. It has two mirror-image body halves. This makes it similar in body plan to the tunicate larva, and unlike the radially symmetrical adult starfish. Most zoologists think that echinoderms, tunicates, amphioxus, and the vertebrates are the evolutionary branchings from the same line of descent.

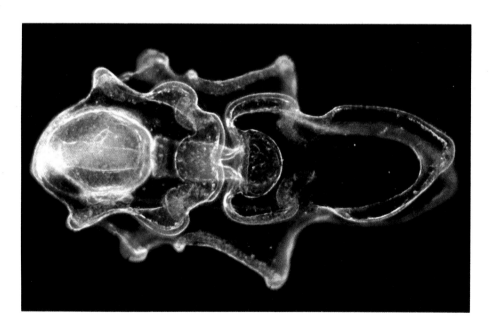

Index *Italicized page numbers refer to illustrations.*